Five for the Land and Its People

Bill G. Reid

North Dakota Institute for Regional Studies

FOR THE LAND AND
ITS PEOPLE

Copyright © 1989
North Dakota Institute for Regional Studies
North Dakota State University
Fargo, USA
Library of Congress Catalog Card Number 88-61399
ISBN 0-911042-37-7

*This work is dedicated to the memory of Dean Harlow Leslie Walster,
who thought these men deserved biographies — and wrote them. Without
his pioneering work this book would not have been possible.*

H.L. Walster

Acknowledgements

The idea for this study was Dean H.L. Walster's. Dean Seth Russell of the College of Arts and Science encouraged me to carry the work further, to write life studies and not just scientific surveys. From his idea, a multi-biography emerged. His successor, Dean Archer Jones, also encouraged the work during his tenure of office.

Perhaps my greatest debt is to Dean Roald Lund of the College of Agriculture, who funded two summers of research on the work and who generously furnished the monies for the publication of this book. Dean Archer Jones, as director of the North Dakota Institute for Regional Studies, accepted the work for publication and it is published under the direction of Margriet Lacy, current dean of the College of Humanities and Social Sciences and director of the North Dakota Institute for Regional Studies.

The manuscript was read and improved by various faculty of the College of Agriculture, by Drs. David Danbom, Michael Lyons and Larry Peterson of the history faculty, by Dean Archer Jones, and by Lou Richardson of the mass communication faculty. An especially heavy debt is owed to Mrs. Richardson, who edited the final version of the manuscript and, with Mark Strand of the Communications Office, saw the work to completion.

The curator of the Institute for Regional Studies, John Bye, kept my desk piled high with material and unfailingly answered my questions.

Of the library staff, Patricia O'Connor spent endless hours helping me locate hard-to-find material. Both the library and the archival staff went beyond simple duty in ensuring the completion of the research.

I cannot close without acknowledging the late President L.D. Loftsgard for his efforts in creating the university atmosphere that made this work possible. Later books, I am sure, will benefit by continued administrative support.

No author likes to face the fact that his or her work is flawed. If I were perfect and the people who generously aided me were infallible, I would not have to admit, nor take responsibility for flaws and errors of commission or omission. Since we are all fallible, I will have to admit the possibility of mistakes and errors, possibly of a grievous nature. I do so, with the firm knowledge that all errors are my responsibility alone and cannot be placed at the door of anyone else.

Table of Contents

Preface

This work relates the life and work of five pioneering agri-scientists of the North Dakota Agricultural College and Experiment Station. The original idea for these biographies was that of Dean H.L. Walster of the College and Station. Walster not only had the inspiration, but he produced lengthy biographies of these five men. They were never published but were deposited in the archives of the North Dakota Institute for Regional Studies. In these portraits Walster confined himself almost exclusively to the professional lives of these scientists. This writer's idea was to produce shorter biographies, make them into a book, and enliven the portraits with personal glimpses of their lives. Some of the personal material is anecdotal, such as how much money L.R. Waldron had when he arrived at the College and Station. Most of the biographical material, though, is sober-sided and factual. From the blend of biography and professionalism there emerges an account of five people who lived in another age, but who are understandable to our generation. At least that is this writer's hope.

The Creation of the Land Grant System and The Founding of the North Dakota Agricultural College

In spite of a democratization of the United States that followed the American Revolution and further democratic reforms during the Jeffersonian Age and the Jacksonian Period, the idea of creating practical colleges for farm and laboring men and women was slow to emerge. The colleges then in existence, and those established in the first half of the 19th century, served mainly the rich, the well-born, and the professional classes. Most colleges were rooted rigidly in the classics. They did not educate along scientific or technical lines.

However, forces at work that made it difficult to reform the old church-related colleges made establishing new institutions inevitable. The Dartmouth Case in 1819, for instance, allowed those colleges to remain free from state direction and control, but schools more responsive to people's needs were being established. The free school idea emerged and spread under such great leaders as Horace Mann, Emma Willard, and Catherine Beecher. As one result Oberlin College threw open its doors to both sexes in 1837. The American Lyceum Movement began in 1826, and such intellectuals as Wendell Phillips brought learning to the masses.[1]

People in the generation before the Civil War wanted to study more than classics and theology. They were interested in science, mathematics, and modern languages, but there was no one to teach them.

So Thomas Clemson, who was later one of the pioneers of the land grant movement, went off to Europe in despair in 1826, because no one in the United States was available to teach him the subjects he wanted to study. These visits to Europe by intellectually thirsty Americans would have an enormous effect upon American science, technology, farming, and the arts.[2] Examining these cultural and intellectual currents furnishes one key to an understanding of America's farming and its handmaiden, the land grant system.

The period in which America achieved its independence has been called the Age of Reason or the Age of Enlightenment. Reason, natural law and progress were idealized as was the nobility of "getting back to nature." At the time of the first U.S. census more than

1

90 percent of all Americans were farm people. Farmers often supplemented their income with craft production, smithing, or plowing for hire, but farming was their primary concern. Farming was their livelihood, but it was also considered the noblest and purest of the professions. It was logical that Americans thought that, but Europeans shared that philosophy. Commoner, noble, and king—all wanted to be associated with the craze of farming. Frederick the Great of Prussia, for example, loved to pose as a rural rustic spouting arcadian thoughts. Not to be outdone, George III of England was fond of the title "Farmer George." Emperor Joseph II of Austria often participated in public plowings, albeit with ceremony, as did Louis XVI of France, and of course, one cannot overlook Marie Antoinette milking her perfumed cow at Versailles. Still, the United States had the only working farmer as chief of state—George Washington.[3]

Washington, Thomas Jefferson, and James Madison all advocated universities tuned to the needs created in the scientific 18th century. Washington proposed a national university and Jefferson thought his greatest personal achievement was the University of Virginia. Jefferson anticipated the land grant system in 1806 when he called for the use of public lands to fund higher education.[4] Madison favored a national university as a part of his new nationalism.

But it was science that ultimately led to a national land grant system. Ironically President James Buchanan vetoed the first Morrill bill designed to create a land grant system the same year Charles Darwin published his *Origin of the Species* in 1859.[5] Darwin's ideas spread and science came to be regarded as more than just descriptive and magical. Most scientists continued to tread warily, however, being afraid that they might offend orthodox Christianity. Fundamentalists were already angered by Darwin's evolutionary teachings.[6] Harvard by 1861 was offering only a few science courses.[7]

Before Darwin there were few scientific institutions in the United States and these were generally concerned with engineering. The U.S. Military Academy opened its doors in 1802, and in 1824 Steven Van Rensselaer founded a technical institute at Troy, New York. It was to be an agricultural school originally, but it developed into a first-class engineering school. Yale and Harvard also established chairs dealing with technology, but colleges generally treated science as they did literature—"to be studied but not used."[8] Few thought that science could be applied to agriculture.

The first exclusively agricultural school was the Gardiner

Lyceum in Maine which opened in 1823. Although it soon failed, it provided a good example. Kings' College (Columbia University) had considered hiring a professor of agriculture as early as 1754. Benjamin Bussey granted money to Harvard in 1823 for a course in "practical agriculture...and in such other branches of science as may be tried to promote a knowledge of practical agriculture and the various subservient arts thereto."[9] Louis Agassiz came to Harvard in 1848 and spent much effort popularizing the study of agriculture.[10]

The need to study and implement scientific farming methods had been forestalled in the United States by the abundance of fertile land. American agriculture at the beginning of the 18th century was wasteful and inefficient partially because of the large supply of rich farming land available to a small population. Southern farmers, for instance, received their greatest profits from one-crop production. But one-crop production was soil depleting especially with tobacco. Soon the tobacco planter found his soil exhausted. In a country with fewer land resources, he might have diversified, fertilized, or gone into cattle or hog production. But in America there was plenty of virgin land in the West. Since the new land was forested, the large southern planter used his slave crews to clear the land and the small planter used his large family for labor. By Washington's time, much of Virginia and Maryland was worn out. Washington, with a lot of land and a surplus of idle slaves, did not retreat west into the forested land as did his smaller neighbors. Instead, he diversified with wheat. He became one of America's greatest agricultural "improvers." Washington was not alone, and national and international crusade movements began.

These movements were based on the fact that farming was indeed the staff of life for most Americans and Europeans. They had a great desire for knowledge that would improve farming and increase output. In England, Jethro Tull used the "horse-hoe" of southern France in his experiments. He advocated more intensive cultivation to English farmers. Lord Townshend improved on Tull's methods, being the first to employ them successfully. Robert Bakewell began systematic breeding of cattle and sheep. Arthur Young argued for more effective methods and a better appreciation of economics. The French also bcame "improvers" with Duhamel du Monceau studying forestry, fungus diseases, and insects.

American leaders realized farming was the primary source of wealth in the United States and would be for a long time. They were also keenly aware of the importance of European innovations.

Benjamin Franklin and the American Philosophical Society encouraged Americans to adopt labor-saving inventions. They believed science would benefit farming. George Washington carried on correspondence with English improvers such as George Young and Sir Arthur Sinclair. He made Mount Vernon a model farm and he carried on lengthy and valuable experiments. Thomas Jefferson was also eager and daring in his farm experiments. He searched Europe for an upland rice for the South, performed rotation experiments, and unsuccessfully tried to introduce olives into America. He also was active in soil conservation work and developed a mold-board plow of least resistance for plowing.[11]

The early American improvers, then, were educated political and intellectual leaders. As such, they had limited contact with dirt farmers. But to advance the movement, they had to find colleagues nearer at hand than England. They succeeded in founding agricultural societies in the eastern United States as early as the 1780s. By 1860, later societies had been vastly democratized.[12]

Agricultural fairs developed in the early 19th century and were a part of the improvement crusade. They sprang from the American rural scene, but had roots back to Medieval Europe. Fairs were a place for farmers to show and sell produce, buy needed supplies, and exchange views with neighbors. Most were local, but fairs such as the Mount Vernon fairs of George Washington Park Curtis had some national status. It was in Pittsfield, Massachusetts, in 1807, however, that the first modern fair and livestock show was held. On that occasion Ilkanah Watson exhibited his prize Merino sheep.[13] Livestock shows stimulated public awareness concerning improvement and brought in converts to the cause.

Of importance, too, to agricultural progress was the proliferation of agricultural journals. The first farm journal was the *Agricultural Museum* founded at Georgetown, D.C., in 1810, which lasted two years. Journals soon spread up and down the Atlantic coast and then penetrated into the rest of the eastern United States. By 1840 agricultural journalism had a toehold in Chicago with the appearance of the *Prairie Farmer*. By mid-century there were at least 40 agricultural papers in the United States. The field was precarious, but its existence meant that more and more farmers would have to be literate to keep up with farm technology. The journals further democratized the improvement crusade.[14]

One thing which made American farmers, and the public, generally accept the need for farm improvement was the prevailing belief in progress, which was closely connected to the concept of

American manifest destiny. It was easy for Americans to move from such views to the idea that American farmers could have an ever-expanding role to play in the United States and in American aggrandizement. Traditional farming methodology was soon supplanted by the belief that farming could change constantly and positively. This led Americans to be particularly eager to adopt labor-saving machines. An official of the Swedish churches in Pennsylvania wrote: "Machines for abridging human labor are especially desired in America."[15] He might have added that natural resources were more plentiful in America than were laborers. Thus, there was no philosophical split with friends in urban centers where labor was also short. Alexis de Tocqueville found that laboring men, as a result, were cognizant of the great pace of technological progress. He wrote: "I once met an American sailor and asked him why his country's ships are made so that they will not last long. He answered off hand that the art of navigation was making such quick progress that even the best of boats would be almost useless if it lasted more than a few years."[16]

Not all American farmers believed in the doctrine of technological progress. Farmers as a rule, though, were more willing to accept new machines than they were to accept scientific ideas. In the 19th century farmers did not struggle against the reaper, the gang plow, or barbed wire fences. They could see what the machines did, but they could not comprehend the benefits of fertilization or plant breeding. Scientific agriculturalists would have to demonstrate their importance. Most agricultural leaders, however, were enthusiastic about science on the farm and its off-spring, technology. Horace Greeley reflected this, albeit with some exaggeration: "TO THE MAN OF OUR AGE, who shall make the first plow propelled by STEAM, or other mechanical power, whereby not less than TEN ACRES PER DAY shall be thoroughly pulverized to depth of TWO FEET at a cost of not more than two dollars per acre."[17] Farmers accepted more and more of the new implements and listened more and more to the experts.

Americans were attuned to the practical, and most of them conceived of science as practical. Could, then, practical science be taught in colleges to enhance agriculture, the nation's basic industry? Some Americans thought so. Plans for a utilitarian college came from the dreams and purses of people who believed practical science could be applied in agriculture and industry. The best-conceived institution in the 1850s was the People's College of upstate New York, which was the plan of Harrison Howard.[18] Horace Greeley furnished enthusiasm for the People's College and suggested courses in applied agriculture, an open country location, and student aid.[19] But the 1850s with its multiplicity of causes was a hard decade for the foundation of a reform college. While reformers were advocating equal rights for women, eradicating slavery, and prohibiting the consumption of alcohol, farmers remained indifferent to the causes of reform on their behalf. In the end only federal aid was able to save the institution.[20] Other colleges of a similar nature included the Ovid Academy, New York, which opened in 1860 and the Farmer's College near Cincinnati, Ohio.[21]

Michigan was the first state to use the land grant system on a state level to found an agricultural college. Agitation for a separate Michigan agricultural college became a reality in 1850, when that provision was inserted into the revised constitution. The Legislature didn't pass enabling legislation providing for such a college until 1855, however. Farmers and the advocates of a separate agricultural college feared the University at Ann Arbor would give slight attention to agriculture so they proposed the agricultural college be located at East Lansing, far from the University, to guarantee an emphasis upon agriculture.[22]

When Michigan Agricultural College's first president, Joseph R. Williams, gave the dedication address in 1857, he was aware that he headed an institution that existed only in the minds of its founders. The campus was forest and mud. There was no academic pattern to follow—not even in Europe—and there was no student body. Still, there was the thrill of pioneering and great expectations.[23]

No one was quite sure what the curriculum of an agricultural college should be, so Michigan aggies took a mixture of manual labor and scholarly work. High schools were nonexistent, so students enrolled in preparatory work. The high school curriculum in 1861 consisted of higher arithmetic, physical and mathematical geometry, and English grammar. For the first year of college there was mathematics, history, English literature, and bookkeeping. The second year introduced students to physics, physiology, horticulture, civil engineering, botany, mineralogy, and inductive logic. As juniors the students studied rural engineering, drawing, geology, mental philosophy, astronomy and zoology. As seniors they took chemistry, political economy, veterinary medicine, agricultural and geographical botany, technology, and household and rural economy. A few women also enrolled in the household and rural economy offering.[24] The Legislature enpowered the faculty to confer degrees in 1861.

What had been created was a tough curriculum combining physical activity with arduous study. But few of the courses were directly related to agriculture since agricultural courses had not yet been developed. Students were exposed to science, history, bookkeeping, political economy, and even astronomy. Gone were Greek and Latin; in were history and English, and physical prowess was emphasized. There was a good deal of fluctuation regarding curriculum in the early days of Michigan Agricultural College. Some presidents liked the classics; others viewed history and English with disdain. Williams was right; there was no pattern to follow.[25] But Michigan helped set a precedent for the federally endowed land grant system.

Other states, including Pennsylvania, Massachusetts, Iowa, and Maryland, took early steps toward creating land grant colleges. The most successful and interesting was the Pennsylvania scheme of Evan Pugh. Unlike the Michigan Agricultural College, which had public support, the Pennsylvania development was Pugh's private scheme. In 1854 the Pennsylvania Legislature authorized a Farmers' High School which became a college by 1862. The college was to train not only farm men and women, but research people and teachers in country schools. Pugh opposed manual labor as a part of the curriculum. He wanted to combine agriculture and mechanic arts in one college. When the Morrill Act was passed Pugh led the fight to make the Pennsylvania Institute part of the land grant system.[26]

Land was the single American national asset belonging to the people. With the Northwest Ordinance, and its companion, the Land Law of 1785, Congress declared the west a national resource. The Northwest Ordinance stated that "education shall be forever encouraged and public land was to be used for that purpose."[27] Both the federal government and the states endowed education through land. As Congress ceded land to the states, the states endowed education with the land. Farmers had always wanted free land for settlers, and in 1862 that goal was attained by the Homestead Act. Republicans, grateful for their victory, added the Morrill Land Grant Act, which made it possible to establish agricultural colleges.[28]

The land grant system was the product of the dreams of two men, Jonathan Turner of Illinois and Justin Smith Morrill of Vermont, although Turner's name has not been as clearly associated with the land grant system as Morrill's has. Turner's daughter noted that her father was interested in a new type of education for agriculturalists and mechanics as early as the 1830s. His thoughts were clearly expressed in 1850 when the Granville conventions met in Illinois. By 1851 he was dreaming of support for such education through federal land grants. In 1853 the Illinois Legislature communicated Turner's ideas to Congress. Horace Greeley quickly supported the Illinois Resolutions. Not many other people were attracted to the idea, but the clarion call had gone out. Turner's plan reflected the dissatisfaction that had been found in Michigan earlier. He stormed: "The old colleges have hauled a canoe alongside their huge professional steamships and invited the farmers and mechanics to jump on board and sail away with them; but the difficulty is they will not embark." Some have referred to Turner's plan as the "common man's education Bill of Right."[29] .

The other idea man was Justin Smith Morrill of Vermont. He grew up in an agricultural state and he was impatient with the old classical education. He knew and approved of Turner's ideas, but his tenure in the U.S. House and Senate gave him advantages Turner never had. Morrill attempted to get his land grant ideas through Congress in the 1850s, but the time was not suitable. An entrenched Democratic Party controlled the presidency, the Congress, and the courts. The slavery situation was tense, and the North and the South each held a veto. The Democratic Party was opposed to free home-homesteads and innovative ideas such as a land grant system. Still, despite opposition and the animosity from such statesmen as Henry Clay, Morrill's bill passed both House and Senate in 1859 only to be vetoed by President James Buchanan.[30]

But things were different after the South seceded. Lincoln and the Republicans were receptive to ideas that would appeal to westerners, farmers, and mechanics. So Morrill tried again. Under the Land Grant Law, neither territories nor rebel states would receive land grants, but the land grant for the northern states was increased. While states received no money for buildings, they were required to create at least one college within five years of acceptance. Land grant institutions also were required to teach military tactics.[31]

The bill passed in June 1862 and had broad support. Farmers thought it was good or at least harmless. The U.S. Agricultural Society approved of it. Educators sensed an increased endowment for higher education. Easterners liked the grant of western land, having used up their own land bounty. Prominent supporters were Marshall Wilder of the Massachusetts Agricultural College and Evan Pugh. Senator Benjamin Wade of Ohio, hoping to attract more farmer votes in future elections, vigorously supported the proposal.[32]

But new opposition was building. With the South absent, it became an east-west battle. Westerners believed it an eastern grab for western land and they felt the land distribution was unfair. They feared eastern land speculation most. However, the measure passed both houses in June and the votes were not especially close.[33]

The president who received the bill for signing was not the arch conservative Buchanan, but the broad constructionist Whig Abraham Lincoln. Lincoln, preoccupied with the war, was glad to accept a program that would benefit both agriculturalists and mechanics even though he was not an especially great supporter of the land grant idea.[34]

Agriculture was being taught, but it was still necessary to form an organization to dispense agricultural knowledge. Such an idea had roots going back to George Washington and the Revolution. The Continental Congress was interested but took no action. President Washington later advised the establishment of a Board of Agriculture, which could dispense agricultural knowledge and seeds. Despite more than 90 percent of the American people being farmers, Washington's request still was not enacted.[35]

A nation of farmers was less interested in agricultural programs than the gentry of the Agricultural Society. Still, progress was being made. Benjamin Franklin began sending back seeds and cuttings from abroad, and other diplomats followed suit, one sending back Merino sheep from Spain. President John Quincy Adams approved of such activity and proposed a national botanical garden. Congress soon set up committees on agriculture in both houses.[36]

In 1836 Henry Elsworth, the commissioner of patents, formalized seed distribution from abroad to "enterprising" farmers. He also set aside $1,000 to collect agricultural statistics, to conduct farm investigations, and to distribute seeds. With this appropriation, Ellsworth established the Agricultural Division of the Patents Office.[37] It was not until 1862 that Congress established a separate governmental office of agriculture. Work had proceeded quietly through state and local societies, the agricultural press, and farmers themselves to convince voters that a separate federal agency was needed. Midwest farmers had helped elect Lincoln in 1860 and they could not be denied their spoils. Lincoln, as a result, called for the creation of an "Agricultural and Statistical Bureau." In 1862 Congress established an independent commissioner of agriculture; however, the first commissioner of the Bureau, Isaac Newton, made few changes from Patent Office procedures.[38]

The growth of the Bureau was evolutionary. In 1871 a librarian was hired, and it was discovered that the Bureau had the best agricultural collection in the country, with 8,000 books on hand. The Bureau issued annual reports, and it sent pamphlets regularly to farmers' clubs, state agricultural colleges, and to individuals on the mailing list. But the Bureau had many political problems and did not receive relief until the passage in 1883 of the Pendelton Act, which founded a civil service.[39]

The Bureau maintained a formidable research staff in the early years. Dr. H.W. Wiley, for instance, was engaged in research on the sugar value of sorghum and D.E. Salmon researched bacteriology. Gradually divisions were established within the Bureau. The first was the chemistry division in 1862, followed by the entomology division in 1878. C.V. Riley began statistical work in the 1860s along with J.R. Dodge, who went to Europe to study the statistical methods there. When he returned from Europe he helped completely reorganize the statistical work, and the statistical appropriation climbed from $10,000 to $80,000.[40]

The Bureau's division of animal husbandry, established in 1884, carried out some of its finest work. The dressed meat industry had boomed with Civil War demand, and cattle kingdoms had grown in the Great Plains, with the establisment of major Northern packing centers and the development of refrigeration. In the 1870s cheaply dressed cattle and hogs were exported to Europe where they wreaked havoc with local producers. Fearing tariff reprisals by the United States if they raised import tariffs, European countries banned American meat products as diseased. American cattle did suffer from pluero-pneumonia and Texas fever, and so Americans quarantined infected animals and the Bureau bought diseased ones to take them off the market. The diseases were soon eliminated and European governments had to find other means of banning American meat.[41]

In 1889 the time had come for cabinet rank for agriculture. Throughout the turbulent 1870s and 1880s farmers through the Grange, the Alliances, and the Populists had petitioned Congress to establish a Department of Agriculture. The popularly elected House routinely passed enabling legislation, but the indirectly elected Senate refused until 1889. Then the force of public opinion compelled that body to act and cabinet status became effective in February 1889. During the same period Congress reflected both rural and urban sentiment when it routinely provided higher Bureau appropriations. By 1894 the appropriation was a little more than

$26 million annually.[42]

The U.S. Department of Agriculture greatly enhanced its image during the late 19th and early 20th centuries. Seed gathering explorations by certain USDA and land grant specialists was one way this was done. Among these experts was M.A. Carleton, who sent back wheat seed from northern Russia. Equally as important was Henry Luke Bolley of the brand new North Dakota Agricultural College, who was best known for collecting flax samples from Europe and Russia for his flax wilt experiments.[43]

The size of the Department was augmented in 1905 when the secretary of agriculture took over the national forests.[44] Between its inception in 1839 and 1917, the Bureau/Department had cost the nation approximately $285 million. Since the country had just about doubled in size during that time and its population had increased about six-fold between 1840 and 1920, the per capita assessment was not very high. The USDA had made available innumerable varieties of crops by importing, developing and refining seeds, had compiled weather records, and had made its research findings available to farmer and nonfarmer alike. Even speaking conservatively, the investment had paid off handsomely.[45]

Dispensing information from the Bureau/Department to farmers was a problem. The land grant colleges had been designed to facilitate this. But it was also necessary to create research centers in the different agricultural regions. The first experiment station was established in 1875 at Wesleyan University in Middletown, Connecticut. This was to provide a two-way linkage between the colleges and the farmers, with the stations engaging in regional or national reserach and passing on the results and the farmers benefiting from the knowledge and techniques. The addition of the extension service would extend information to the farmers and complete a three-way tripod of education, research, and extension.[46] The Magna Carta for the stations was the Hatch Act of 1887,[47] which provided funds for the creation of experiment stations connected with the land grant colleges.[48]

While the legislation that would make agricultural colleges and their experiment stations and extension services possible was being passed, Dakota Territory, which would be so affected by those institutions, was being settled. Dakota Territory was founded in 1861, one year before the passage of the Morrill Act. The background for the founding of the North Dakota Agricultural College and Experiment Station is to be found in American settlement patterns and the establishment of Dakota Territory. The founding of North

Dakota Agricultural College and Experiment Station coincided, not quite, but near enough, with the development of the farm tripod.

The Homestead Act and the Morrill Act were, unfortunately for the Middle and Far West, based on conditions that prevailed in the humid, forested land east of the Mississippi River. Morrill and the other promoters of the land grant system were thinking of the climate and environment at Michigan Agricultural College— not the grass-covered plains of Dakota. Supporters of the Homestead Act had envisioned a 160-acre homestead in a humid, forested area that would support a family. But when Governor William Jayne, and his successors, arrived at Yankton in southern Dakota Territory, they found a grass-covered prairie. Early farmers settled only in the bottom lands where there were trees for housing, fire, and fencing. Most farmers thought prairie land was worthless for farming and as eastern farmers migrated west, they had bypassed the plains of Illinois and the deltas of the South. They skipped over the "Great American Desert" to settle in California and Oregon, and areas such as Utah that could be irrigated. Only with time and new technology would they come into the Great Plains. When they did, starting in the 1870s, they rapidly settled the plains as the railroad, the elimination of Indian power, the killing off of the buffalo, and the invention of barbed wire fencing, the windmill, and suitable plows made the settlement of the Great Plains a three-decade affair.[49]

If early settlers weren't interested in farming the prairies, how would they make their living in Dakota? Profits from speculation, trapping, and Indian trade were available, but not for everyone. They had an economic problem, which some settlers thought they could solve by manipulating government affairs and living by political means. Dakota settlers remembered the schemes over the location of a federal capital and wondered if there was an essential difference in locating a territorial capital at Yankton. Having a territorial institution in a newly formed city would guarantee that city's prosperity, they thought. The Dakota Territory capital at Yankton was looked upon as something that would open up jobs in an area where farming was probably not profitable. But the schemes to locate the capital were nothing compared to those for locating a penitentiary in a territory where there were few felons and even fewer law officers. County seat selections also were hotly contested. So Dakotans saw government as the ultimate economic source in a barren land.[50]

Dakota was not to remain agriculturally barren for long, however. Settlers from Iowa and Minnesota eased into the southern

12

part of the territory and by the 1870s and 1880s it was evident that a mixed agriculture could be profitable. Settlement in the northern part of the territory developed mostly because of the railroads. By 1873 the Northern Pacific had reached Bismarck, Dakota Territory. In that year, Jay Cooke and Company collapsed causing outstanding railroad bonds to become worthless. The railroad's land agent, James Buel Power, developed a scheme to trade off the railroads' land grant railroad securities. As northeastern financiers bought up the securities they found themselves in possession of vast amounts of potentially good wheat land in the Red River Valley of the North. Spring wheat, which grew well in the Valley, was inferior for milling flour until an agent for eastern milling interests, George C. Christian, obtained a new milling process that made spring wheat suitable for flour. Overnight the Bonanza farm phenomenon flowered in the Red River Valley, where the most famous of the Bonanza farm managers was Oliver Dalrymple.[51]

It was northern Dakota's development and some political shenanigans that ended with the removal of the territorial capital to Bismarck in 1883 that whetted appetites for institutions in the northern part of the territory.

Fargo was the largest city in northern Dakota and although it was Republican, it was politically split into two factions—headed by Samuel G. Roberts and Major Alonzo Edwards. The only thing that unified the factions was an insatiable appetite for governmental institutions. It was Roberts who persuaded the southerners to duplicate existing southern institutions in the north in 1883. At the end of the territorial legislative session that year, Grand Forks received the university, the penitentiary went to Bismarck, and Jamestown secured the insane hospital.[52] The location of an agricultural college at Fargo was agreed on but no money was appropriated for it.[53]

The boomer town of Fargo, known as the "Biggest Little City in the World," almost spurned the idea of a local agricultural college. After all, hadn't the Congregationals been eager to establish a private college there? Why have such a mundane thing as a college for young farm people? Roberts lobbied for the agricultural college, but he contended with the attitude that "it would be better to abandon any attempt to secure its (agricultural college) location and go for something of greater benefit, an Indian school, or a school for the deaf and dumb, or a school of science, something big."[54] Fargo ended up having the agricultural college thrust upon it.[55]

The Constitutional Convention for North Dakota was

dominated by "interests looking for favors."⁵⁶ Political leaders such as Alexander McKenzie and Jud LaMoure vigorously lobbied for their localities. United localities such as Grand Forks were adamant about including their institutions in the Constitution. The leaders in 1889 were not at all concerned with what Elwyn B. Robinson would refer to as "too much mistake" (trying to do too much too fast with too little). They wanted jobs and prosperity for the settlers; let the future take care of itself.⁵⁷ Another decision that would affect the state was included in the Constitution in 1889. North Dakota would follow the earlier action of Michigan in establishing a separate university and agricultural college, the former for classical studies and the latter for agriculture and engineering. The University had been staffed in 1883 with a faculty and administration with degrees from traditional institiutions but although it emphasized a classical education, the University was often called Grand Forks College in its early days and was little more than a liberal arts college and normal school.⁵⁸

Establishing a separate agricultural college in the Constitution was, of course, a break with tradition, just as it had been in Michigan. If funded, it would create a new institution that must be built and staffed. The Constitution had made the "too much mistake" a possibility; now when the money was appropriated it would be a reality.⁵⁹

As far as the 1890 Legislature was concerned, a separate agricultural college had been part of the Dakota Territory precedent. The Territorial Legislature in 1889 introduced a bill to provide for the college but the measure was vetoed because the governor felt the college was not needed nor was there any money to pay for it. The bill of 1890 was passed on the grounds that the institution would begin its life based upon securing a federal Experiment Station appropriation.⁶⁰

The governor appointed a Board of Trustees for the new institution, the most important members being O.W. Francis and S.S. Lyon, both of Fargo, and James Buel Power of Power. Francis was an attorney dealing with tree claims and abstracts. He was the owner of a handsome farm in Traill County and he represented the Red River National Bank in the courts. Power was a believer in a mixed agriculture of grains and livestock and he practiced that type of farming at his Hellendale farm at Power. He held an important position as land agent for the Northern Pacific Railroad and he had handled the exchange of bonds for land during the Bonanza period. S.S. Lyon was a promient banker of Fargo and was very active in the affairs of the infant First Presbyterian Church of Fargo.[61] The Board of Trustees was more concerned with establishing an experiment station than an agricultural college.

Meyer and Meyer refer to 1862 as the "annus mirabilis" of American agriculture, because in that year the Homestead Act and the first Morrill Land Grant Act were passed.[62] Farmers, at least on paper, received a great deal in 1862. In what Rossiter refers to as "Slow Beginnings" the new legislation did have a liberating effect upon the agricultural sciences.[63] When North Dakota Agricultural College took up temporary residence in Fargo in 1890, the situation in agricultural science was much brighter than in 1862. Darwin's theory of evolution was now held by most scientists and students of Asa Gray were sprinkled all over the nation expounding the "new botany." Many of these young men were "farm boys with Midwestern degrees" and this was especially true of two men who came to North Dakota Agricultural College in 1890—Clare Bailey Waldron and Henry Luke Bolley, both of whom were new botanists. Such young men had a sense of destiny; they eagerly taught their students, did their research, and just as eagerly sought the professional approval of their president and director and their colleagues elsewhere.

Equally stimulated was the science of horticulture where Liberty Hyde Bailey in academia and Luther Burbank in private practice were doing work that would create a professional horticulture.[64] Bailey was to be a great teacher and an outstanding administrator. The new North Dakota Agricutural College received his student Clare Bailey (C.B.) Waldron, who had training in horticulture. Waldron was also the first entomologist for the North Dakota Experiment Station and that field had made strides.[65]

Agricultural chemistry also expanded, specialized, and took on new tasks in the decades leading to 1890. In 1880 the Association of Official Agricultural Chemists was formed, primarily to standardize tests and measurements. Most of the new experiment station men had to test fertilizers sold within their states and they needed to coordinate their tests and to work for uniform laws. By the time Edwin F. Ladd located in Fargo in 1890 he was using a complex range of tests. Finding much produce abuse he, like many agricultural chemists, drifted over into the complex and controversial pure food and drugs field.[66]

John Henry Shepperd came to the North Dakota College and Station in 1893 to succeed his brother-in-law Willet M. Hays as Hays had moved from Fargo to become director of the Minnesota

Experiment Station. The rediscovery of Mendel's theories of genetics had a stimulating effect on Liberty Hyde Bailey and his experiments in horticulture and, thought Hays and Shepperd, why couldn't they be applied to livestock breeding? Hays was a "hustler" and a "booster" and he founded the American Breeder's Association in 1903 to promote livestock breeding. In 1910 the association started the popular *American Breeder's* magazine. Always in contact with his brother-in-law, the quieter Shepperd gravitated toward livestock work, although as the College's agriculturalist, he did other things as well.[67]

Waldron, Bolley, Ladd and Shepperd formed the nucleus for agricultural research and education in the founding days of NDAC. They were joined in 1915 by Lawrence Root Waldron, who came to the Fargo campus as plant breeder. Although this was the only position he held at the College and Station, his prolific development of varieties of hard, red spring wheat stems partially from that specialization. He benefited from the foreign expeditions of Bolley of NDAC and of Mark Carleton of the USDA and the rust and drought resistant varieties they brought back with them.[68] He also benefited from Mendel's genetic breakthrough, and he received his Doctor of Philosophy in Genetics from Cornell in 1928. Today he ranks as patron saint of agronomy at North Dakota State University.[69]

Building the road near College Hall at NDAC (later called Old Main) ca 1892.

Old Main ca 1900

Footnotes

[1]Edward Danforth Eddy Jr., *Colleges for Our Land and Time,* (New York: Harper & Brothers, 1957), pp. 5-6.

[2]*Ibid.,* pp. 6-7.

[3]Paul H. Johnstone, "Old Ideals Versus New Ideals in Farm Life," in *Yearbook of Agriculture,* 1940, pp. 112-114, surveys the Age of Enlightenment.

[4]Eddy, *Colleges for Our Land,* p. 7.

[5]*Ibid.,* p. 8.

[6]*Ibid.,* pp. 9-10

[7]*Ibid.,* pp. 9-10.

[8]*Ibid.,* pp. 10-11.

[9]*Ibid.,* pp. 12-13.

[10]*Ibid.,* p. 13.

[11]Johnstone, "Old Ideals," pp. 113-114.

[12]*Ibid.,* p. 114.

[13]*Ibid.,* p. 115.

[14]*Ibid.*

[15]*Ibid.,* p. 124

[16]Edited by J.P. Mayer and Max Lerner, a new translation by George Lawrence, Alexis de Tocqueville, *Democracy in America* (New York: Harper and Row, 1966), p. 420.

[17]Johnstone, "Old Ideals," p. 155.

[18]Eddy, *Colleges for Our Land,* p. 15.

[19]Earle D. Ross, *Democracy's College,* (Ames: Iowa State College Press, 1942), p. 22.

[20]*Ibid.,* through p. 26 for the complete story of the People's College.

[21]Eddy, *Colleges for Our Land,* p. 16.

[22]*Ibid.*

[23]*Ibid.,* pp. 16-17.

[24]*Ibid.,* and John N. Winburn, *A Dictionary of Agriculture and Allied Terminology* (East Lansing: Michigan State University Press, 1962), p. 716, and Edward L. Schapsmeier and Frederick H. Schapsmeier, *Encyclopedia of Agricultural History* (Westport, Connecticut: Greenwood Press, 1975), p. 322, for definitions of the Smith-Lever and Smith Hughes Act.

[25]*Ibid.,* p. 18.

[26]*Ibid.,* p. 19.

[27]*Ibid.,* p. 31.

[28]*Ibid.,* p. 22.

[29]*Ibid.,* pp. 23-26.

[30]*Ibid.,* pp. 26-32.

[31]*Ibid.,* p. 33.

[32]*Ibid.,* p. 34.

[33]*Ibid.,* p. 35.

[34]*Ibid.*

[35]E.E. Edwards, "The First 300 Years," USDA, *Yearbook of Agriculture, 1940*, (Washington: United States Government Printing Office, 1940) p. 246.

[36]*Ibid.*

[37]*Ibid.*, p. 247.

[38]*Ibid.*, pp. 248-249.

[39]For the tangled history of the public domain and education one should consult: Marion Clawson, *The Land System of the United States: An Introduction to the History and Practice of Land Use and Tenure* (Lincoln, Nebraska: University of Nebraska Press, 1968), and Benjamin Horace Hibbard, *A History of the Public Land Policies* (New York: The MacMillan Company, 1924).

[40]E.E. Edwards, "The First 300 Years," p. 249-250.

[41]*Ibid.*, p. 250.

[42]*Ibid.*, p. 251.

[43]*Ibid.*, p. 252

[44]*Ibid.*, pp. 252-253.

[45]*Ibid.*, p. 253.

[46]Margaret W. Rossiter, "The Organization of Agricultural Sciences," in Alexandra Oleson and John Voss, editors, *The Organization of Knowledge in Modern America, 1860-1920* (Baltimore, Maryland: Johns Hopkins University Press, 1979), p. 214. Also Andre Meyer and Jean Meyer, "Agriculture: In-land Empire," *Daedalus* 103 (Summer 1974) p. 88.

[47]*Ibid.*, pp. 215-216.

[48]*Ibid.*, p. 215

[49]The idea for the settlement of the Great Plains and Dakota Teritory is taken from Howard Roberts Lamar, *Dakota Territory, 1861-1889: A Study of Frontier Politics* (New Haven: Yale University Press, 1956), the Preface. The readers should also consult Walter Prescott Webb, *The Great Plains* (New York: Grossett and Dunlop, 1931).

[50]*Ibid.*

[51]William C. Hunter, *Beacon Across the Prairie* (Fargo: North Dakota Institute for Regional Studies, 1961), p. 7.

[52]*Ibid.*, p. 9.

[53]*Ibid.*, p. 10.

[54]*Ibid.*, p. 13.

[55]*Ibid.*

[56]*Ibid.*, p. 12.

[57]*Ibid.*, pp. 12-13.

[58]*Ibid.*, p. 15.

[59]*Ibid.*

[60]*Ibid.*

[61]*Ibid.*, pp. 16-17.

[62]Andre Meyer and Jean Meyer, "Agriculture: In-land Empire."

[63]Rossiter, "The Organization of the Agricultural Sciences," p. 240, and

Andrew Denny Rodgers III, *American Botany 1873-1892: Decades of Transition* (Princeton, New Jersey: Princeton University Press, 1944) for the "New Botany."

[64]Rossiter, "The Organization of the Agricultural Sciences," pp. 224-226, for Bailey and Burbank.

[65]*Ibid.*, p. 223, and North Dakota Agricultural College Catalog, 1901.

[66]*Ibid.*, Rossiter, "The Organization of the Agricultural Sciences," p. 215.

[67]*Ibid.*, pp. 226-227. See also the John Henry Shepperd Papers, NDIRS, for the Hays-Shepperd relationship.

[68]Rossiter, "The Organization of the Agricultural Sciences," p. 215, and for Carleton and L.R. Waldron Papers, NDIRS.

[69]L.R. Waldron Papers, NDIRS.

Clare Bailey Waldron

Clare Bailey Waldron: Scientist as Apostle of Outdoor Beauty

Although the state Legislature had established an agricultural college and experiment station at Fargo, the institution had no home nor staff, and it faced a local citizenry not very friendly toward the new entity. Perhaps Major Alonzo Edwards, editor of the *Fargo Argus*, summed up Fargo opinion best when he wrote: "The Board of Trustees of the North Dakota Agricultural College—whatever that is—met yesterday and elected a faculty—whatever that is—they will at least increase the population."[1] The five members of the Board of Trustees with Attorney O.W. Francis of Fargo as president elected Dr. Samuel T. Satterthwaite, a retired physician in Fargo, as temporary director of the Experiment Station on May 15, 1890.[2] The first faculty member, Clare Bailey Waldron, whom they appointed as botanist for the college and station, reported for duty July 19, 1890.

Most of the young agriculturalists of the 19th and early 20th centuries could be characterized as "largely government employees and more often farm boys with midwestern master's degrees than Ivy Leaguers with German doctorates."[3] Except that Waldron's postgraduate work had not earned him a master's degree, this description fit him perfectly. Not only had he been a farm boy, but later Dean Harlow Leslie Walster of the North Dakota Agricultural College was to write: "Boy he was when he first landed in North Dakota."[4] On October 15, 1890, the College Board approved nominations for the faculty. They were Waldron, 24, Michigan Agricultural College, professor of horiculture and forestry; Henry Luke Bolley of Purdue, 24, professor of botany and biology; and Edwin F. Ladd, 31, of the University of Maine, professor of chemistry. [5]

All of the young faculty were farm-bred and from the Midwest, except for Ladd who was from a Maine farm. They were newly educated, enthusiastic about their work, and committed to improving and developing North Dakota. Waldron himself once wrote a short history of the college wherein he expanded on the youth factor: "The whole situation was a demonstration of youthful enthusiasm and ambition which may account for the early prominence and success of the institution."[6] Waldron also recalled the spirited exchange of views among the young faculty as to the importance of their respective fields. He referred to these exchanges as a "favorite indoor sport."[7]

The new faculty served under another young man, Dr. Horace E. Stockbridge, who was only 33 when he came to NDAC as president of the College and director of the Experiment Station in August 1890. Though young in years, Stockbridge had ample experience. His ability and youthful enthusiasm enabled him to guide the College in its first faltering steps. To him goes the credit for the first college short courses. He was active in designing the administration building, "Old Main," and he had a hand in planning the engineering building and Francis Hall.[8] As director of the North Dakota Experiment Station, he encouraged the work of the staff. The North Dakota Station was somewhat typical of other states, but elsewhere "devoted researchers" were "eclipsed daily by the more aggressive and assertive bureau chief or station director (who might be a former politician or editor untrained in the sciences)." But in North Dakota, President Stockbridge did not "eclipse" the young researchers. Perhaps Stockbridge's scientific background and experience elsewhere, atypical of directors of stations in the 1890s, explains his fostering the work of his young colleagues and giving them full credit.[9] He established an important tradition in this respect.[10]

Stockbridge was born in Hadley, Massachusetts, in 1857, received his training at Massachusetts Agricultural College and attained his doctorate at Gottingen University in Germany. In the 1880s he was associate professor of chemistry at Massachusetts Agricultural College, from which he went to Japan to become professor of chemistry and geology at the Imperial College of Agriculture and Engineering until 1889. During his last two years in Japan he served as chemist for the Imperial Japanese government.[11] After he returned to the United States he became director of the Agricultural Experiment Station of Purdue University, coming to Fargo in August 1890 and remaining until May 1893.

The attempt of the Populist governor of North Dakota, Eli C.D. Shortridge, to remove conservative members of the Agricultural College Board brought Dr. Stockbridge's administration to an abrupt end. These members resisted removal, an ugly investigation followed, and a court case confirmed the right of board members to hold office until their tenure expired. When the dust settled Stockbridge was the most obvious casualty, having been removed.[12]

Leaving North Dakota, Stockbridge went to Florida where he became professor of agriculture at the state college until 1906. As one of the founders of the *Southern Ruralist*, he served as its editor for a number of years. He was a member of the National Agricultural War Conference, was president of the Farmer's National Congress at one time, and wrote several books on chemistry of the soil.[13]

The first of NDAC's young staff to arrive in Fargo was C.B Waldron. He had graduated from Michigan Agricultural College where he had studied botany and horticulture. He had done two years of postgraduate work at Michigan Agricultural College, but had not attained a postgraduate degree.[14] When the Fargo offer came, he was doing "landscape engineering" work in Duluth, Minnesota.[15] Later Dean Walster referred to Waldron's Duluth position as a "bread and butter" job that through the filter of time came to be called landscape engineering. Undoubtedly Waldron was planting trees and trimming hedges while in Duluth.

In 1890 Fargo was not far removed from frontier days. Waldron's mother had warned him not to go to that "awful" place of Fargo where he might be blown away by tornadoes or scalped by Indians. When he arrived at the railway station, Waldron must have been sharply reminded of his mother's advice because freight cars were lying on their sides by the track—blown there by the most recent tornado. To increase his discomfort, Indian braves in full-dress regalia were sitting by the station. Whether it was the need for a permanent job or bravery that motivated him, Waldron elected to stay.[16]

No college or experiment station existed in a physical sense when Waldron arrived. He wrote: "Picture in your mind's eye a field of golden wheat in Section 36, Fargo Township, with no buildings to mar its botanical beauty."[17] The college and station land was separated in 1890 by farmland from the city.[18] Director Satterthwaite's and Waldron's offices were on the third floor of the Red River Bank at 11 Broadway and the first college classes were held in the basement of Fargo College, the Congregational college.

The Board members exhibited much more enthusiasm concerning an experiment station than they did about a college because a station seemed more practical and the Hatch Act of 1887 had made federal money available. Therefore, Waldron began work on a temporary assignment for the station while awaiting appropriation of state funds for the College.[19]

His work called for "classifying, preparing, and mounting the material collected on field trips from the South Dakota border to the Turtle Mountains." This collection became the beginning of the herbarium of the Agricultural College. In the fall seeds from the collection were sown on the College grounds. The work was continued in 1891 with the collaboration of Henry Luke Bolley, who came to the institution in October 1890.[20]

Clare Bailey Waldron, known as "C.B.," was born December 6, 1863, in Ravenna, Ohio. While he was still a boy, his family moved to a fruit farm near Ionia, Michigan. After graduating from the Palo, Michigan, high school in 1884, Waldron entered Michigan Agricultural College, completing a bachelor of science degree in 1887. For the next two years he did postgraduate work at Michigan Agricultural College.[21]

While studying botany at Michigan Agricultural, Waldron came under the influence of W.J. Beal, professor of botany, curator of the Botanical Museum, and botanist to the Experiment Station.[22] Beal, who was born in 1833 in frontier Adrian, Michigan, was one of those believers in the "old botany" who transferred their loyalties to the "new botany." New botany was the expansion of the field from simple taxonomy (classification of plants and animals) to a broad science influenced particularly by Darwinism. Beal had studied first under Louis Agassiz, a naturalist of the old school, but later Asa Gray at Harvard easily converted him to Darwin's theories of evolution. In 1871 he went to Michigan Agricultural College where he taught until his retirement. He probably did not influence as many students as did the famous new botanist Charles E. Bessey at Nebraska, but he had charisma and did influence such students as Waldron. His best work was *The New Botany*, published in 1881, but his two-volume *Grasses of North America* was the most famous. Unfortunately, the work, marred by errors, created as much confusion as enlightenment. This was the man, then, who made a new botanist out of Waldron.[23]

But Waldron's training was broader than simply botany, because he had branched out into horticulture studying under Liberty Hyde Bailey. Bailey, with the possible exception of Luther Burbank, was the most eminent horticulturist in America.

The nationally known Bailey was a son of Michigan, having been born in Van Buren County in 1858. He attended South Haven, Michigan, public schools and Michigan Agricultural College, receiving his B.S. in 1882. In 1883 he became assistant to the famous Asa Gray at Harvard, although he attained no degree there. In 1885 he accepted a position as professor of horticulture and landscape gardening at his alma mater, receiving his M.S. from Michigan

26

Agricultural College in 1885. At a time when botanists looked down on horticulture, he took a leading role in developing horticulture as a separate and respectable science.[24]

In 1888 Bailey went to Cornell University, becoming involved there in practical and experimental horticulture. An excellent teacher as well as researcher, he sought to impart to New York farmers the basics of plant cultivation. Promoted to dean of the Agricultural College in 1903, he began to exert the magic that astounded Waldron. He quickly built an outstanding agricultural college. When he resigned his deanship in 1913, he donated his herbarium, which included 125,000 specimens, to Cornell. Taken all in all it would be fair to state that this excellent teacher, researcher, and administrator was the dominant force in Waldron's academic training. Bailey's significant ideas, through Waldron, influenced North Dakota.[25]

In later years Waldron wrote concerning Bailey: "I entered Michigan State Agricultural College the year that Dr. Bailey took charge of the department and took courses from him in general horticulture, landscape gardening and orcharding. In my seventh (probably sixth year) he gave me a special assignment of compiling notes on the development and flowering of all the woody plants on the campus. He used to have a few students at his home frequently."[26]

Years later Waldron wrote: "The writer was privileged to take several terms of horticulture under Dr. Bailey, and to assist him in some of his research. On a visit to him later, when he was dean of the College of Agriculture of Cornell University, it was interesting to learn that this man of science had, almost single-handed, wrested from a reluctant legislature, largely of city men, the several hundred thousand dollars necessary to equip what has since continued to be one of the great agricultural institutions."[27]

Bailey came to North Dakota during the time he was chairman of the Country Life Commission, and Waldron took him on a tour of the eastern part of the state. Impressed with the rich farm land, Bailey nevertheless argued against the one-crop cultivation of wheat.[28] Bailey also visited North Dakota Agricultural College in 1920 as a part of a college lecture course.[29]

In later years Waldron had much to say concerning conditions at the early-day Agricultural College, including sports, which for the first year or two were carried on in an unfinished floor of Old Main. To the athletic activity of the young professors, Waldron attests: "The unfinished upper floor of Old Main was used as a gymnasium where tug-of-war, wrestling and boxing were the prevailing sports. The faculty members were young enough not to have lost their skill in such contests, as some of the over-ambitious could ruefully testify."[30]

Because of the small size of the agricultural faculty, the young professors found themselves teaching a wide variety of subjects. They attempted to ensure that each student received a liberal as well as a practical agricultural education. Waldron wrote: "In the course of a year the same instructor might be expounding to the same students the mysteries of the starry heavens and the heights and depths of the earth and the living things thereon, the doings of the Greeks and Romans, not to mention the Dutch and the Irish, the solemn satisfaction that lies in the solution of differential equations and the secrets of the skill by which writers and orators move the multitudes."[31] Rather whimsically Waldron reflected that he did not know whether the early students received a liberal education, but he expressed his certainty that the faculty did and that midnight often found their coal oil lamps burning.[32]

Part of Waldron's recollections concerned the state of agricultural science in the 1890s. He said there was not enough agricultural science in existence in 1890 to construct a respectable curriculum. Agricultural methods, too, were largely a matter of folk practice that had been handed down from generation to generation. The men in agricultural science such as Waldron, Bolley, and Ladd had necessarily received their training in the pure sciences of botany, horticulture, and chemistry. Only horticulture approximated an agricultural discipline and Liberty Hyde Bailey and others were striving to make it more scientific. Some people even felt there should be no instruction in agriculture itself at agricultural colleges. They believed instruction should be in the pure sciences, with an occasional agricultural flavor. But the scientists at North Dakota Agricultural College never made that mistake.[33]

Waldron wrote that in 1890 plant and animal breeding were primarily games of chance, with no set laws having been discovered. Few plant diseases had been identified and agricultural economics was an untitled academic field. Agriculture from a business viewpoint could only be guessed at. Textbooks, or what passed for textbooks, were totally inadequate and the only laboratory equipment was for the pure sciences. In that time instructors had to wander far afield to have enough to fill their lecture and laboratory hours.[34]

Still it was an exciting period for agricultural science. Darwin's theories were known, at the turn of the century Mendel's findings would be rediscovered, and the agricultural sciences were making rapid strides. Those stressed at the Agricultural College and in the Experiment Station were horticulture, animal nutrition and husbandry, and botany. Agronomy did not develop as a separate science until the turn of the century.

This was also a period of increase in federal money expended on agricultural research and in the development of agricultural specialties and organizations, and of a dramatic increase in the number and prestige of agricultural scientists. Federal expenditures dated back to the land grant system and the Morrill Act of 1862 and the Second Morrill Act of 1890. The Hatch Act of 1887 and the Adams Act of 1906 both provided generous federal expenditures for experiment stations. Government increased its agricultural expenditures from $1,708,000 in 1890 to $2,623,000 in 1894.[35]

Certainly there were difficulties for the new North Dakota Agricultural College and its program. Still the young professors lobbied constantly for the largest possible share of appropriations and allocation of faculty. Waldron recalled it thus: "Curriculum making in those days was the favorite indoor sport. It was always in season and the contenders only stopped short of broken heads."[36] Subjects that were not in the core curriculum, such as mathematics, English and history, were apportioned out according to the availablity of a certain man at a certain hour. Waldron wrote: "If it so happened that a stolid, plodding scientist was expected to be transformed into a fiery rhetorician upon an hour's notice it was all a part of the day's work."[37]

Since there were no formal extension personnel in the early days, the youthful professors were expected to carry on that work. This was probably fortunate, for they learned the problems that needed solving and became acquainted with the work conditions in the state.[38]

Life for the young professors was not all work. There was time for social activities, and for Waldron very soon romance and marriage. In the formal language of days gone by, W.C. Hunter, the historian of the Agricultural College, wrote: "C.B. Waldron became the escort and soon the husband of the president's secretary, Lois Hooper."[39] Miss Hooper was also the first librarian of the Agricultural College.[40] She was born November 7, 1861, and spent her formative years in Portland, Maine. She was a graduate of the State Normal School in Maine before coming to Fargo in 1888 where she was one of the pioneer teachers. She exchanged vows with Mr. Waldron December 24, 1891.[41] The Waldrons had a significant role in the early social and cultural life of Fargo. Mrs. Waldron was a member of the Fine Arts Club of Fargo for many years and was a civic leader in step with her active husband.[42] Both were members of the Unitarian Church.

The *Spectrum*, the student newspaper, reported that in June 1912 they entertained the graduating seniors of the college with a lawn party and supper at their home. The party featured the beautiful flowering shrubs on the Waldron lawn and each senior was given a bouquet.[43] Another *Spectrum* report said that in 1916 they were surprised at their home by a college group that presented them with a gift of silverware in honor of their 25th wedding anniversary. The guest list read like a Who's Who at the Agricultural College that year. It included President and Mrs. Edwin F. Ladd, Dean and Mrs. Henry Luke Bolley, Professor and Mrs. John H. Shepperd, and Mr. Thomas Cooper, the director of the Experiment Station, among others. Although 1916 was the year of the "Hearing of 1916" and a ferocious struggle between Bolley and Cooper, nevertheless both attended the social event.[44]

On the family level, the Waldrons often entertained younger brother L.R. Waldron, who was superintendent of the Dickinson Station until he became plant breeder for the home station at Fargo in 1915.[45] There were three children—Eloise, who taught English at the Agricultural College; Clarence, who had a seed testing laboratory at Toledo, Ohio; and Max, who managed citrus groves near Fort Lauderdale, Florida.[46] Mrs. Waldron died May 30, 1932, after a long period of illness.[47]

Aside from his social, church, and family activities, Waldron was active in professional and service organizations. He was prominent in the Polytechnic Society, which was primarily a discussion group mostly of College faculty that met every two weeks to hear a paper read. The Society was founded in 1907 and remained active until 1925.[48] Waldron was president in 1909.[49] He was especially active in the North Dakota State Horticultural Society and was elected president of the organization in 1909. His colleague, Professor O.O. Churchill, was secretary and treasurer at the same time.[50] Another professional organization that claimed a portion of Waldron's time was the North Dakota Education Association. When the group met in Grand Forks in 1915, Waldron presided over the Department of Science and Mathematics.[51] He was president of the Tri-State Grain Growers Association and was re-elected president in 1917.[52] In 1920 NDAC President-emeritus John H. Worst replaced Waldron as president of the Grain Growers Association as Waldron's duties with the Army at that time took precedent.[53] At one time he was also president of the North Dakota Academy of Science.[54]

As the third decade of the North Dakota Agricultural College approached, Waldron found himself busier than ever. In 1910 Governor John Burke appointed Waldron as his representative to the Conservation Congress in St. Paul, Minnesota. This was the conference where Gifford Pinchot, president of the National Conservation Association, battled in favor of former-President Theodore Roosevelt's policies of conservation against "state's right conservationists" and the more conservative followers of President William Howard Taft. The crest of progressive insurgency came in 1910 and it should be noted that Roosevelt's supporters received more applause than did Taft's at the Congress.[55] The North Dakota delegation to the Congress elected Waldron as chairman of the North Dakota Conservation Convention that was to meet in Fargo.[56]

Waldron attended professional conferences, as well, among them the American Pomological Society (the science of fruit cultivation) and the American Society of Horticulture meetings in 1913.[57]

Administrative duties beckoned Waldron in 1915 as he was chosen by the Agricultural Board of Trustees as dean of agriculture at North Dakota Agricultural College.[58] He succeeded John H. Shepperd, who was unhappy with the new organization that had placed Thomas Cooper as director of the Experiment Station in 1914. Shepperd was himself a conservative, however, and was, therefore, in philosophical agreement with the conservative Cooper, as we shall see later. Shepperd was transferred to the Experiment Station in 1920.

Waldron's administration of the School of Agriculture brought a period of gradual growth, with departments of agricultural education, animal nutrition, agricultural economics, and agricultural engineering being added. The great dream of a separate building for agriculture was realized in 1922 when the first unit of the agricultural building to be called Morrill Hall was completed. During the period he was dean, the School of Agriculture and Waldron were separate from the Experiment Station.

Meanwhile the outbreak of World War I in 1917 meant additional duties for Waldron. In May 1917 Governor Lynn J. Frazier appointed Waldron to the State Council of Defense, which had charge of war prepartions and sought solutions for food problems.

To spur the economy of a nation at war, Congress conferred upon President Woodrow Wilson an unprecedented power to regulate the American economy. The president in turn delegated these powers to a series of boards under the Council for National Defense. The states during World War I also set up state Councils for Defense. Waldron's particular role in the state Council was as chairman of the agricultural committee, for which he was most eminently qualified.[59] The Army at this time planned to convert Army camps into vocational training schools and Waldron was put in charge of the agricultural part of the plan. He served about a year and a half in this developmental work.[60]

Waldron served as dean of agriculture for nine years until June 1924 when he went back to his former position as professor of horticulture, forestry, and landscape gardening.[61] He was replaced as dean by Harlow Leslie Walster, who would distinguish himself over the years. Walster was born at Troy, Wisconsin, on April 20, 1883, and attended high school at Spring Green, Wisconsin. His bachelor's degree was from the University of Wisconsin, his master's from Harvard, and his Ph.D. from the University of Chicago. He came to North Dakota Agricultural College in 1919 after serving as instructor and professor of soils at the University of Wisconsin. With his earned doctorate, he was evidence of the increase in specialization at the Fargo institution. He became dean of the School of Agriculture in 1924, but it was not until 1934 that he became director of the Experiment Station.

In addition to his duties as horticulturalist and forester, Waldron was called upon to be the Agricultural College's first entomologist. He taught courses in entomology for a number of years and from his private accumulation he started the college's insect collection. In 1898 he published the Station's first bulletin on insects, "Some Destructive Insects." In it he described the grain aphid, the wheat stem maggot, the Hessian Fly, the fruit fly, the army worm, and grasshoppers, including the Rocky Mountain Locust.[62]

Even earlier, in July 1891, Waldron had written Special Bulletin No. 1, "Rocky Mountain Locusts."[63] In this bulletin he described the locusts and other grasshoppers and outlined methods of control. One was the hopperdozer, which was a large mounted iron pan filled with water and an oil film. As the hopperdozer was pulled through an area, insects hit a canvas barrier, fell back into the solution and died. On one occasion he recalled catching more than a hundred bushels of half-grown hoppers.[64] Waldron also recommended an alternative method of destroying hoppers with a poisoned bran mixture. The poison bait was made by adding one-fourth of a pound of Paris green to a bushel of any bran. To this was added one gallon of molasses and enough water to moisten well. But the best way to destroy the pests, according to Waldron, was to plow under the stubble where the eggs were deposited in the fall.[65] He had the support of the Northern Pacific and Great Northern railroads in his anti-grasshopper campaign.[66] After the 1890s, hoppers did not become a problem in North Dakota again until the 1920s and 1930s when poisoned bran was again broadcast by spreader or by hand.

Waldron was, of course, interested in all insects that did damage to the farm economy. In 1900 he reported: "An insect that did far greater damage in the state last year than the grasshoppers have done in all the years is the Hessian Fly."[67] Still, Waldron speculated that the Hessian Fly was not considered a serious menace in spring wheat belts, especially at a high latitude with a dry climate. Most wheat growers were familiar with the Hessian Fly in its pupal stage, often called the "flaxseed" stage because the pupa was as tiny as a flaxseed. The insect at this stage causes the lower joints of the wheat stalks, usually the second one above the ground, to break over just as the wheat is ripening. As the wheat is harvested, practically all of the "flaxseeds" are left in the stubble; therefore, Waldron advised that the best method of controlling the Hessian Fly was to plow under the stubble.[68] In the long run he was correct for there was only one minor outbreak of Hessian Fly from 1919 to 1955.[69]

While the original plans for the College grounds were drawn by A.W. Spalding, a landscape gardener, Waldron planted the trees. W.C. Hunter states: "Waldron also drew plans for the College grounds, and, with the help of H.W. McArdle, planted the trees which now shade the driveways and walks of the campus."[70] Walster relates: "Many of the trees which C.B. Waldron planted on the campus of the North Dakota Agricultural College were grown directly from seed which he planted, or were transplanted as yearly saplings."[71]

Waldron had a profound impact on the beautification of Fargo as well as the Agricultural College. Fargo's parks owe much to his contributions.[72] He helped create the Fargo Park Board in 1910 and served continuously on that board until 1945.[73] His foresight on park matters allowed Fargo to buy park land while it was possible. Waldron spent an infinite amount of energy promoting his various park projects.[74] He involved his landscape gardening classes in observing and participating in park beautification. In 1915, for instance, his class observed what was being done with the southside Island Park and the students also studied work being done around private housing.[75]

Waldron's work with beautification and public parks spread out from Fargo to the rest of the state. He was particularly active in beautifying school grounds and special instititions. These included Kindred Public School, Minot State Teacher's College, School for the Feeble Minded at Grafton, School for the Deaf at Devils Lake, Bathgate's School for the Blind, and the Industrial and Normal Institute at Ellendale.[76]

His work with parks and other public grounds included the courthouse grounds at Lisbon and public parks in Jamestown, New Rockford, and Edgeley.[77] Walster claims work on the International Peace Garden as one of Waldron's achievements.[78] If Waldron did play a role in the Peace Garden, however, it was so minor that his name never appeared in contemporary documents. In a paper concerning the Peace Garden, Keith Allan Johnson, a North Dakota State University student, correctly notes that James V. Freeham of Minneapolis was the original landscape architect for the garden. Waldron did criticize Freeham's plan because it had features which "would not ordinarily be expected in a public garden in this part of the country."[79]

In addition to park, school, and public building adornment, Waldron was active in bringing trees to pioneer homesteads. Farmers planted many miles of trees furnished by Waldron and the College in shelter belts and hedges in the early part of the 20th century. Waldron reported in 1905: "Last spring something over two hundred thousand of the Golden Russian willow were sent to farmers in different parts of the state." In the same year he went to the Badlands to obtain native red cedar for planting at the College and Station. He was especially interested in conifers for planting because they enlivened the landscape, both in summer and winter[80] but he admitted that conifers presented special problems when planted on the open prairie, and the young conifers would have to be protected by older trees.

Waldron was always proud of his work regarding black walnuts because the trees were beautiful and they produced rich nuts. He had originally obtained seed nuts from the R.M. Probstfield farm in Minnesota.[81] Waldron also directed the tree planting (snowguard) program of the Great Northern Railroad along the Surrey Cut-off.[82]

Waldron realized that trees grown on the Northern Great Plains would of necessity have to be drought-resistant to survive in a semi-arid environment. By 1911 he noted: "Studies would indicate that drought-resistant trees are the western conifers like the yellow pine, Colorado spruce and red cedar; the deep-rooting trees like the ash and walnut, and trees with a special type of foilage like the Russian wild olive."[83] He realized that only trees adaptable to the fierce, continental climate of North Dakota would grow well there.

Coming from the fruit-producing region of Michigan, horticulturalist Waldron set out to find fruit-bearing trees that would adapt to the Northern Great Plains environment. Climate was the greatest barrier to fruit production in North Dakota. Severe winters killed the trees, the heavy soil did not warm up rapidly in the spring to support their growth, and late spring frosts killed the young fruit. Waldron's research was hindered most notably by lack of greenhouses and laboratory equipment and by the fact that the state did not appropriate adequate funds. Still, he persisted in his efforts. He worked continuously with seedlings of the native wild plum from 1891 to 1913 and made some progress. But his research on the wild plum finally was brought to an end by the lack of greenhouse facilities needed for hybridization with other species to obtain firmness of flesh.[84]

Like most horticulturists and landscape gardeners, Waldron was interested in fairs and exhibitions. He was a member of the committee to study the College's participation in the Chicago Exposition in 1893, and he visited that show. In addition he was chosen for the jury of awards for the Louisiana Purchase Exposition in St. Louis and for the Lewis and Clark Exposition in Portland, Oregon, both in 1905.[85]

Waldron was not as prolific a writer as Henry Luke Bolley or John H. Shepperd, but he worked very hard to popularize what was known about horticulture. During the years 1900 to 1911 he was a constant contributor to the *North Dakota Farmer's Institute Annuals*. The *Annuals* were readily available to the public, in particular practicing farmers. He wrote many articles for the *North Dakota Farmer* from 1902 to 1917, and he served that publication as editor of a section titled "Shade Trees and Gardens." He wrote regularly for the *North and South Dakota Horticulture* from 1930 to 1944. His last article, cited earlier in this chapter, was a tribute to his mentor, Liberty Hyde Bailey.[86] He clearly was most successful in bringing up-to-date horticultural information before the public.

While some prophets are without honor in their own countries, this was not true of Waldron, for the College awarded him an honorary degree, the Doctor of Agriculture, in 1939. The award was written and read by Dean Walster at the 45th commencement.[87] When Waldron retired from his many college duties in 1945, a bronze bust of "C.B." was presented to the College with a good deal of ceremony. The bust was the work of Ida Bisex Prokop of Lidgerwood, North Dakota, who had sculpted busts of other promient North Dakotans.[88] Soon after his retirement and the presentation of the bust, Waldron moved to Fort Lauderdale, Florida, to live with his son, Max. Almost two year later, "C.B." died on March 6, 1947.[89]

C.B. Waldron spent much of his early years at NDAC transplanting American elms from along the Red River to the campus. This first tree-planting ceremony took place ca 1892.

C.B. Waldron was dean of agriculture and one of the speakers when the cornerstone for Morrill Hall was laid in 1922.

The first NDAC employee, C.B. Waldron devoted his entire working life to the college. He was a member of the faculty from 1890-1940.

A northwest view of the experiment plots and horticultural gardens ca 1920. Francis Hall, now demolished, is in the foreground.

C.B. Waldron ca 1940

Footnotes

[1]Henry Luke Bolley, "Early Days at the A.C.," *College and State,* November 1923, p. 11.

[2]William C. Hunter, *Beacon Across the Prairie: North Dakota's Land-Grant College* (Fargo: North Dakota Institute for Regional Studies, 1961), pp. 16-17.

[3]Margaret W. Rossiter, "The Organization of the Agricultural Sciences," in Alexandra Oleson and John Voss, editors, *The Organization of Knowledge in Modern America, 1860-1920* (Baltimore, Maryland: Johns Hopkins University Press, 1979), p. 240.

[4]H.L. Walster, "Faculty Chat—Apostle of Outdoor Beauty," *The Spectrum,* December 9, 1938.

[5]Hunter, *Beacon.* The ages are given in Chapter II of this work. Dean Harlow Leslie Walster, in a fictionalized portion of Waldron's biography, had C.B. saying that he preferred horticulture to botany. This, however, is not sound historical data.

[6]C.B. Waldron, no title, no date, "History," p. 7. In the C.B. Waldron Papers, *NDIRS.*

[7]*Ibid.,* pp. 6-7.

[8]"First President of the College Passes in Georgia City," *The Spectrum,* November 11, 1930.

[9]Rossiter, "Agricultural Sciences," p. 220.

[10]Hunter, *Beacon,* p. 28. A strong argument might be made that he was "more scholarly and better trained than most" of the presidents who followed him.

[11]*Spectrum,* November 11, 1930.

[12]*Ibid.* and Hunter, *Beacon,* pp. 27-28.

[13] *Spectrum,* November 11, 1930.

[14]Hunter, *Beacon,* p. 18. For more details of Waldron's education see H.L. Walster, "Clare Bailey Waldron—Horticulturist—Apostle of Beauty" in *Five For the Land.* Consult also H.L. Walster, "Faculty Chat—Apostle of Outdoor Beauty," *The Spectrum,* December 9, 1938.

[15]Walster, "Apostle of Beauty," p. 2.

[16]"Waldron Recalls Old Times at N.D.A.C.," *The Spectrum,* February 28, 1941.

[17]*Ibid.*

[18]*Ibid.*

[19]Hunter, *Beacon,* p. 18.

[20]Walster, "Apostle of Beauty," pp. 2-3.

[21]*Ibid.,* pp. 1-2.

[22]*Ibid.*

[23]Allen Johnson, editor, *Dictionary of American Biography,* Vol. I (New York: Charles Scribner's Sons, 1964) pp. 87-88.

[24]The biographies are: Phillip Dorf, *Liberty Hyde Bailey: An Informal*

Biography (Ithaca, New York: Cornell University Press, 1956) and Andrew Denny Rodgers III, *Liberty Hyde Bailey: A Story of America's Plant Sciences* (New York: Hafner Publishing Co., 1965). For biography given in these pages consult: John A. Garraty, editor, *Dictionary of American Biography,* Supplement Five, 1951-1955 (New York: Charles Scribner's Sons, 1977). p. 30.

[25]*Ibid.*, pp. 30-31.

[26]*Botany Newsletter,* Volume V, No. 6, reprinted as 29th *Annual Report* of the South Dakota State Horticulture Society, 1942, p. 18.

[27]C.B. Waldron, "Liberty Hyde Bailey," *North and South Dakota Horticulture,* Volume XVII, March 1944, p. 42.

[28]*Ibid.*

[29]*The Spectrum,* December 18, 1919.

[30]"History," p. 6, Waldron Papers, NDIRS.

[31]Clare Bailey Waldron, "Campus Recollection: After Viewing an Old College Album," *College and State,* Volume 8, No. 2, November 1924, pp. 15-16.

[32]*Ibid.*

[33]C.B. Waldron, "Little Acorns and Great Oaks," *College and State,* Volume 7, No. 2, November 1923, pp. 1-2.

[34]*Ibid.*, p. 2

[35]Edward E. Edwards, "American Agriculture—The First 300 Years," *Yearbook of Agriculture,* USDA, 1940, 251. See also Rossiter, "Agricultural Sciences," pp. 212-213.

[36]Waldron, "Little Acorns and Great Oaks," p. 2.

[37]*Ibid.*

[38]*Ibid.*

[39]Hunter, *Beacon,* p. 27.

[40]"Dr. Waldron Dies in Florida; was Early A.C. Faculty Member," *Fargo Forum,* March 7, 1947.

[41]*Ibid.* and "Mrs. Waldron Dies in Fargo," *Fargo Forum,* May 31, 1932.

[42]"Dr. Waldron Dies in Florida."

[43]*The Spectrum,* June 4, 1912.

[44]"Waldron's Twenty-Fifth Anniversary," *The Spectrum,* January 10, 1916.

[45]*The Spectrum,* December 20, 1910, March 28, 1911, and February 20, 1912.

[42]"Dr. Waldron Dies in Florida."

[43]*Ibid.*

[44]Hunter, *Beacon,* p. 42.

[45]*The Spectrum,* June 1, 1909.

[46]*The Spectrum,* January 26, 1909.

[47]*The Spectrum,* November 10, 1915.

[48]*The Spectrum,* January 24, 1917.

[49]*The Spectrum,* January 27, 1920.

[50]"Unveil Bust of C.B. Waldron at Graduation Monday," newspaper clipping, no date, Waldron Papers, NDIRS.

[51]*The Spectrum,* September 27, 1910.

56*The Spectrum*, November 25, 1913.

57*Ibid.*

58Walster, "Apostle of Beauty," p. 21. For Walster see biographical note, NDSU. Furnished by Experiment Station Central Office.

59*The Spectrum*, May 2, 1917. On Council for National Defense, see: Richard L. Watson, Jr., *The Development of National Power: The United States, 1900-1919.* (Boston: Houghton-Mifflin, 1976).

60Newspaper clipping, no name of paper, no date, Waldron Papers, NDIRS. The source says "war years," but it was probaby the immediate "post wars" years.

61Annual Report of the North Dakota Agricultural College, 1918.

62Walster, "Apostle of Beauty," p. 15, and Clare Bailey Waldron, "Some Destructive Insects," in Bulletin 34, North Dakota Agricultural Experiment Station, 1898, pp. 293-304.

63Clare Bailey Waldron, "Rocky Mountain Locusts," Special Bulletin No. 1, North Dakota Agricultural Experiment Station, July 1891, pp. 9-11.

64*Ibid.*, p. 11. For a drawing of the hopperdozer consult Waldron, "The Grasshopper Past," Special Bulletin, North Dakota Agricultural Experiment Station, May 1911.

65Waldron, "Some Destructive Insects," p. 298. Waldron did not consider the poisoned bait very effective. Waldron, "Rocky Mountain Locusts," p. 10. He thought plowing was most effective.

66C.B. Waldron, no title, no date, "History," p. 6.

67Tenth Annual Report of the North Dakota Agricultural Experiment Station, February 1, 1900, p. 49.

68*Ibid.*, pp. 49-50. C.B. Waldron, "Some Destructive Insects," p. 294.

69Walster, "Apostle of Beauty," pp. 16-17.

70Landscape Map of College by W.W. Spalding, 1891, NDIRS, and Hunter, *Beacon*, p. 48.

71Walster, "Apostle of Beauty," p. 5. For bibliography N.D. Agricultural College, Experiment Station Bulletin, No. 34, December 1898.

72"Unveil Bust of C.B. Waldron at Graduation Monday," No name of paper, June 1945, Waldron Papers, NDIRS.

73Hunter, *Beacon,* p. 48.

74"Dr. Waldron Dies in Florida."

75*The Spectrum*, November 6, 1915.

76Walster, "Apostle of Beauty," p. 19.

77*Ibid.*

78*Ibid.*

79Keith Allen Jacobson, "The International Peace Garden," History 405, North Dakota State University. Waldron was probably talking about a proposed peace tower which would not fit well into the natural landscape.

80Walster, "Apostle of Beauty," p. 6.

81*Ibid.*, p. 7.

82*Ibid.*, p. 19.

83*Ibid.*, p. 15.

[84]*Ibid.*

[85]*Ibid.*, pp. 17-18.

[86]*Ibid.*, p. 20.

[87]Walster, June 5, 1939, in Waldron Papers, NDIRS.

[88]"Unveil Bust of C.B. Waldron at N.D.A.C. Graduation Monday," No name of paper, June 10, 1945, in Waldron Paper, NDIRS.

[89]"Dr. Waldron Dies in Florida."

Henry Luke Bolley

Henry Luke Bolley: Scientist as Conqueror of Flax Wilt and Founder of North Dakota Football

Among the original faculty was Henry Luke Bolley, a young botanist and plant pathologist. He was fresh from earning his master of science degree from Purdue University when he arrived in Fargo in 1890. There is no written record that Bolley intended to make the newly organized North Dakota Agricultural College and Experiment Station his permanent career and home, but that is exactly what happened. From 1890 to 1948 Bolley's activities had an important effect on North Dakota agricultural development. His work was intensely pragmatic, but his methods were scientific. Bolley pioneered in flax wilt research, formaldehyde treatment for smuts of grain, chemical spraying of weeds, and common potato scab research. He crusaded for better and purer seed, and he researched the problem of typhoid in water and milk. He also did experiments in tree feeding.[1]

Bolley's background was English, his parents John and Mary (Broad) Bolley having come to America in 1848.[2] Born February 1, 1865, young Bolley was reared on a farm with his sisters and brothers in St. Clair County, Michigan.[3] He was the 12th child of a large family, and often the struggle for existence was a sharp one.[4] Recalling those days, Bolley said: "I began trying to help myself and mother get a living at the age of eight when and where I could get work, but because of the persistence of a broad-minded mother and of sisters and brothers, I was never allowed to permit this to interfere with the period allowed for going to school."[5] This encouragement well complemented the young Bolley's insatiable appetite for learning, particularly about nature and its workings.[6]

His education was punctuated by work on farms, at a time when many people believed that such seasoning was necessary to becoming a successful agriculturist. At the end of his secondary education, he was awarded the Dearborn County scholarship to Purdue University, the first such scholarship.[7] At Purdue Bolley met stimulating teachers in botanical sciences, such as Dr. Stanley Coulter and Dr. J.C. Arthur.[8]

Professor Arthur, an exponent of the "new botany," particularly had a profound effect on the young man. The scientific world had been accustomed to viewing all species as immutable because they had been created by God. But in 1859, Darwin's *Origin of the Species* exploded upon the world of science as though a bomb had been set off. That species could and did evolve through the "survival of the fittest" had a revolutionary impact on the biological sciences. Young scientists tended to accept the new doctrine more readily than did their older colleagues. But it was the distinguished botanist Asa Gray of Harvard whose defense of the new theory made it acceptable. Gray was measured in his arguments and the fact that he was an orthodox Christian helped turn away objections based on the theory's apparent conflict with the Bible. Many accepted evolution because of Gray's arguments.[9]

Still it was not until the 1870s that the new botany began to evolve. Prior to that time young botanists were urged to study medicine in order to have a livelihood to support their "hobby." Professor Arthur was definitely in the school of the new botany. While at Iowa State in 1870 he began taking courses under Dr. Charles E. Bessey, who became one of the most radical of new botanists. Later at Harvard, Arthur studied under the eminent Harvard botanist, Dr. William G. Farlow, and with Asa Gray himself. When Bolley came to Purdue, Arthur was best known for his work on plant rusts and he was the first to use formaldehyde for preventing potato scab. Bolley was the first in a long line of botanists influenced by Arthur.

Bolley was born and reared in an academic sense in the new botany. His interests were wide and he used Darwin's thesis to good advantage. As a student at Purdue, Bolley concentrated on the diseases of wheat and potatoes.[11] As might be expected of a student of Arthur's, he wrote his master's paper on the nature of the rusts of the cereal grains.[12] While at Purdue Bolley served as assistant botanist and plant pathologist at the Indiana Experiment Station and as a student aide in the physics and biology laboratories.[13]

Bolley first heard of North Dakota Agricultural College and Experiment Station from Dr. Horace E. Stockbridge, then director of the Indiana Experiment Station and newly elected president of the North Dakota institution.[14] Bolley recalled that Stockbridge was enthusiastic about opportunities for agricultural scientists in North Dakota and he told Bolley he wanted a plant pathologist and botanist to join him in Fargo. Stockbridge said: "The two great crops of North Dakota are wheat and flax. Aside from your teaching you should have plenty to do."[15] Later Bolley was to remark: "I have had plenty to do." Bolley decided to take the North Dakota opportunity and he wrote many years later: "My studies...had been concerned primarily with the diseases of wheat and the diseases of potatoes. It is needless to say, therefore, that I was delighted with the great opportunities possible to the plant pathologist and botanist in the new, almost virgin lands of North Dakota."[16]

Bolley arrived in Fargo a few days before October 15, 1890. It was raining when he got off the train at the Great Northern Depot in Fargo and he took a two-horse taxi down Broadway where he saw the deepest black mud he had ever seen. Riding in the same carriage was Edwin F. Ladd, the new chemist. This was Bolley's first meeting with the future advocate of pure food and drugs.[17]

Simultaneous with the arrival of Bolley and Ladd, a group of prominent Fargoans and North Dakotans was meeting. This first meeting of the Board of Trustees of the Agricultural College and Experiment Station was held in the office of O.W. Francis in the Red River Valley National Bank. No one knew what the agenda would be, but the Board elected the first faculty of the Agricultural College and the staff of the Experiment Station at that meeting. The next morning Major Alonzo W. Edwards of the *Fargo Argus* published his oft-quoted sarcastic remarks about the new institution: "The Board of Trustees of the North Dakota Agricultural College— whatever that is—met yesterday and elected a faculty—whatever that is—they will at least increase the population."[18]

Not at all daunted by Major Edward's sarcastic humor, the new institution set up headquarters in the basement and first floor of the main Fargo College building. Soon the young scientists had a passable chemical laboratory and another laboratory for investigations in bacteriology and plant pathology.[19]

Bolley's youthful enthusiasm, aided by his versatility, had some non-academic effects on the young Agricultural College. One was his importation of the manly sport of football from Purdue. A football league in Indiana in the early 1880s had become defunct by 1883. A new league was formed in 1886-1887, in which Purdue participated. The game was enthusiastically supported by Indiana men who had discovered the sport while being educated in Ivy League schools. These men became the coaches for the new Indiana teams. Bolley had played in a crucial 1889 game between Purdue and Wabash.[20]

When Bolley came to Fargo he discovered that an old opponent in the Purdue-Wabash game, botanist M.A. Brannon, was then serving at the University in Grand Forks. Brannon eagerly proposed that the Indiana tradition of zestful football games should be transplanted to North Dakota. Possibly the sting of the Purdue victory of 1889 caused him to seek revenge. But the Agricultural College did not have enough students for a team in 1890. In was not until 1894 that Bolley was able to field a team and reach an agreement with the University providing for a game and a return game each year. The Agricultural College won the 1894 game but in 1895 the two institutions divided the honors.[21]

Years after the first game in 1894, Engineering Dean E.S. Keene recalled that the faculty organized a social for the Aggie victors. He wrote: "We planned a reception for the boys. It consisted of oyster stew, bread and butter and coffee and a good time."[22] Robert Reed, the first Agricultural College student and a member of the first team, remembered the game vivdly. He said: "When the University team came down here the (first) fall they were nicely equipped with stocking caps and our boys were bareheaded, but our team had the stocking caps when the game was over. They did not forgive us for a long time."[23] Reed recalled that the University was short on manpower and the military instructor was drafted to fill out the ranks. This gave the Agricultural College the opportunity to enlist its veterinary teacher, Therieo D. Hinebauch, to complete the team. Hinebauch had joined the NDAC faculty in the winter of its first year.[24] Reed said regarding Hinebauch: "He was good at the art of falling down or stumbling and he always had one or two opponents under him when he fell."[25]

Bolley had introduced the Purdue gravel pit type of football and it was played in a more physical way than the present-day game. Reed recalled: "There was no forward pass in the early days and bucking the line was the main feature. Very little kicking was done. The ball was usually forced through the lines and there was some running around the ends. The game was less complicated and there were fewer penalties. Professor Bolley developed a criss-cross play which worked very well and served to confuse the other team."[26] Early games between the Agricultural College and the University were not just competition between institutions, they also embodied the spirit of the two rival Red River cities, Grand Forks and Fargo.[27]

Later, a loose confederation was formed with schools in South Dakota, but the Agricultural College also played the Minnesota Normal School at St. Cloud, the University of Montana, Creighton of Omaha, Fargo College, and Marquette in Milwaukee. Although he dropped his coaching duties in 1900, Bolley remained as general manager until 1909.[28] Gradually young men who had played high school football enrolled at NDAC, but Bolley and later coaches still had to depend primarily on raw recruits from the farms. By 1896 there were enough interested students that faculty were no longer needed to fill out the team.[29] The Agricultural College exhibited its appreciation of Bolley when it established a football medal in his honor in 1900.[30]

In 1934 a former member of the early teams wrote a letter of appreciation to Bolley. He recalled the factor of inexperience, writing that the members of his team should have been dubbed "The Impossibles" at the time Bolley took charge of them. He believed that more credit was due Bolley than could or would ever be given to him.[31] In spite of the good result he obtained, Bolley conducted his sports program at very little expense. In 1900 the *Spectrum*, the student newspaper, estimated that the total cost for athletics was $202.[32] Before he was finished, Bolley had established a football tradition at the Agricultural College and in the state. Present-day fans are indebted to the likes of the Agricultural College's Bolley and the University's Brannon.[33]

Bolley exhibted another side of his character when he entered into Fargo social life with zest. W.C. Hunter described a bobsled party that took place on H.F. Miller's place northwest of Fargo. The guests were faculty members with their dates from the Agricultural College including Bolley. The party started at 6 p.m. and ended at 4 a.m.[34] While the College was still housed on the campus of Fargo College, Bolley met Miss Frances Sheldon, who was a member of the faculty of Fargo College. As preceptress of Greek and Greek history, the future Mrs. Bolley was educated far beyond the average woman of the day. Few women attended college in the late 19th century, and most of those who did attended normal schools.[35] Miss Sheldon hailed from Wisconsin and had come to North Dakota as a pioneer in education at Fargo College. After a rather long courtship they were married in 1896. The couple had an adopted son and daughter, Don and Ann.[36] Mrs. Bolley died in August 1930 in Argentina where she had accompanied Bolley on a flax inspection trip. In 1931 Bolley married a sister-in-law of his first wife, Mrs. Emily Sheldon. The second Mrs. Bolley died in 1944.[37]

In 1901, 11 years after the College and Experiment Station opened their doors, Bolley wrote to a colleague in Vermont a letter remarkable in its candor, describing the Agricultural College and especially the Botany Department.[38] The institution was a young one in a new and undeveloped region. The students often had very little academic background, since attendance at country schools was difficult because of the work necessary to develop a homestead. Bolley summarized what the College had to deal with by saying that students often brought with them "only a good mind poorly trained." Such conditions led to the fact that much of the education at the College was preparatory and even in the College proper it took much patience to "hold the work down upon a good substantial basis." College work was also hampered, according to Bolley, by the fact that so many students left the College before completing their work, because their labor was needed on the farm.[39]

Referring to his own work, Bolley said he was in charge of teaching botany and zoology for the College and that he served as botanist for the Experiment Station. He noted that he usually had one to two assistants, but they changed rapidly and the amount of unsupervised work they could do varied. He noted that the system required a good deal of work on his part.[40] What Bolley didn't say was that because of the inadequacies of his assistants he had to do many of the simple unprofessional tasks that were necessary in his work.

Writing about the College proper, Bolley noted that he had acquired all the apparatus he needed to carry out his work. The new science hall, later to be called Minard Hall, would soon be ready and the rooms and laboratories would be more than adequate.[41] His previous assistant, L.R. Waldron, was pursuing graduate work at the University of Michigan. When Waldron returned he would join the staff.

Bolley noted that the Agricultural College had few graduate students, the emphasis being placed on developing a strong undergraduate course of study. Specialties included the biological group, the chemical group, and the general science group. General college courses such as language, history, and philosophy were also offered. Bolley said that juniors and seniors selected the line of work that was most suitable for their interests. Students were combined into large groups for lecture and quiz work, while laboratory work was individually directed. He wrote that his ex-students were found in many lines of activity. Some were in medical school, others were teaching in colleges, and one had made himself an authority on dairying work. But most by far farmed.

As for his Experiment Station work, Bolley wrote that in the last year he had gotten less experimental work done than usual, although he was planning more activity in the future. He noted that the usual procedure was to concentrate on one or more lines which seemed most apt to lead to positive results. In the last year the Station had published a preliminary list of seed-bearing plants of North Dakota, and he thought he was on the right track in finding the cause of flax wilt, which had been the reason flax could not be cropped continuously. He believed the disease was caused by a species of Fusarium.[42] He mentioned nothing of L.R. Waldron's work on the seed-bearing plants of North Dakota.

Answering his correspondent's query about the relationship between the Station and College work, Bolley wrote that a man doing both kinds of work could be very useful. The experimenter would receive the benefit of an interested audience and might be spurred on to other research. He noted, however, that the individual should have sufficient aid both in his teaching and experiments to obtain high-level results. Still, he found nothing incompatible with the dual role.[43]

Probably Bolley's greatest claim to scientific fame rests upon his solving the problem of flax wilt. This puzzling phenomenon had been observed widely and had led to the general conclusion among farmers and agriculturalists that continuous cropping of flax led to flax-sick soil. Since North Dakota was an important flax state, the interest among the agricultural scientists at Fargo in the problem was more than passing. Flax, then and now, was used mainly for linseed oil for paint and fiber for linen cloth, although the flax grown in North Dakota was used more for manufacturing cigarette paper and stationery than for cloth. John Henry Shepperd, who came to Fargo in 1893, brought flax disease to the attention of agricultural scientists at Fargo. He recalled: "In the winter of 1890-91 when I was a student in the University of Minnesota, I chanced one day to be in the greenhouse used by Otto Luger of the Minnesota Experiment Station in St. Paul and I saw three beds of flax planted side by side. The two outside beds of flax had good even strands of nice healthy vigorous flax plants, three to four inches high; while those in the middle bed were yellow, wilting and turning brown. I asked Dr. Luger what had happened to the sick and dead flax plants, and he replied, "I wish I knew." That clear-cut trial stuck deep in my memory and three years later, upon coming to this college, I told E.F. Ladd, chemist, and H.L. Bolley, botanist, about it."[44]

It was Shepperd who first proposed to crop "plot 30" continuously to flax until a flax-sick soil was produced, but it was Bolley who carried the experiment through to its successful conclusion. A.C. Dillman, in the 1936 Yearbook of Agriculture, had this to say about Bolley's flax work: "In 1900 H.L. Bolley of North Dakota determined that flax wilt was caused by a parasitic fungus, which he segregated, described, and named. Bolley's work is classical. He was probably the first man in the history of agriculture to submit plants to an epidemic of disease in order to obtain selections resistant to disease. This method makes deliberate use of the principle of the survival of the fittest.... Bolley's work completely altered the outlook for flax production in this country."[45]

The full name of the causal organism of flax wilt is Fusarian oxysporum Lisp Lini (Bolley) Snyder and Hansen.[46]

Dillman was probably unaware of the pioneering work on flax wilt being done by a student scientist on the other side of the world in Japan. In 1902 Bolley received a letter from Kingo Muyabe, Sapporo Agricultural College, informing him of the flax-wilt work of his student, N. Hiratsuka. He wrote: "With great interest, I have read a short review of your paper on the 'Flax Wilt'...which reached me this morning. The same disease occurs in Japan, and has been a nuisance. One of my pupils, N. Hiratsuka studied the fungus in my laboratory some six years ago, and vertified (sic) it to be a species of fusarium and by a series of field experiments came to a the (sic) conclusion very much like yours. I shall send you his paper, although written in Japanese."[47]

Professor Muyabe related that Hiratsuka was a graduate of his college, class of 1892. The student had spent his spare time in Muyabe's laboratory and in his postgraduate days studied mainly plant diseases. The correspondence led to an exchange of professional papers.[48]

Whether Bolley or the Japanese student was first in flax-wilt research is not nearly as important as the fact that their research was parallel. As early as the late 19th century and the early 20th century, Americans and Japanese were in one scientific community.

Bolley's knowledge of flax wilt grew constantly. He suggested that flax-producing areas of Europe be investigated for flax selections. In 1903 the United States Department of Agriculture sponsored his trip to Europe and Bolley spent about nine months in the flax-growing regions of Europe. He had earlier believed that he could develop more wilt-resistant species from Old World samples than he could from American strains, and samples obtained on the European trip gave him an opportunity to test that thesis.[49] Bolley's travels included Holland, Belgium, Germany, and Russia. He visited the botanical gardens of the University of Amsterdam and the University of Munich, and in London he studied the collections of Kew Gardens. He also visited farms, experiment stations, and seed exporters to satisfy his unending curiosity.[50]

Rust was another problem flax growers faced and after exhaustive studies Bolley reached the conclusion that wilt-immune flax plants were just as apt to succumb to rust as common wilt-prone varieties.[51]

Rust is caused by fungi living off the host plant. All countries that produce wheat, rye, oats, barley, or flax are susceptible to rust and occasional extensive crop destruction. A rust epidemic occurs where there are spores, enough moisture, and proper temperature for more germination. Rust spores produce spots on the host plant with the color determined by the rust variety.[52]

Still, even with the rust complication, Bolley's explorations were an enormous success. Returning to Fargo he noted with some pleasure that he had available for testing about 240 flax samples. He later wrote up his conclusions in a bulletin titled "Flax Culture." In that bulletin he noted that for the period 1901 to 1904 North Dakota had produced 50 percent of the nation's flax crop.[53] Officials of the USDA had been eagerly awaiting Bolley's manuscript and he received a congratulatory letter when he finished the work.[54] One result of Bolley's research was the reversal of the belief, both in America and Europe, that flax production was only good on new land, with production falling with successive plantings. He was able to develop new varieties that remained wilt resistant even when planted on old land.

Taking all factors into account, the European trip paid off handsomely. Bolley and his aides developed a number of new flax varieties as a result of the samples he collected and their hybrids and from the information about flax he learned. The first selection that Bolley designated as wilt resistant was his NDR 22. A photograph of the selection was made in 1904, comparing it to common wilt-prone flax.[55]

Bolley's interest in flax and plant diseases was an enduring one. In 1930 he was authorized by the Agricultural College and acting-President Shepperd to make a South American tour, much like the European tour of 1903. Bolley's assignment included full pay and he was instructed, upon returning to Fargo, to conduct extensive investigations on the specimens he brought back. Mrs. Bolley and daughter, Ann, were to accompany him. In making plans, Mrs. Bolley noted: "Everyone around the Bolley house is brushing up on Spanish these days in preparation for the forthcoming expedition."[56]

Bolley's trip was interrupted when his wife died suddenly in Argentina but after accompanying her body back to North Dakota he returned to Argentina and brought back some 409 samples of flax. He wrote up his findings in "Flax cropping in Argentina," December 1931. Bolley outlined in the study his goals for breeding disease-resistant varieties with high oil content that had high drying quality when used in paints.[57]

Bolley's research also included work in taxonomy, the classification of plants. In December 1900 he published with L.R. Waldron, who had just received his B.S. from the Agricultural College, "A preliminary list of the Spermatophyta, seed-bearing plants of North Dakota." The eminent Agricultural College botanist, O.A. Stevens, writing in 1950 in his *Handbook of North Dakota Plants*, said that Bolley and Waldron "listed 775 species of plants which had been collected in the state." He added: "This is approximately three-fourths the number known to occur here." This student-professor venture, then, added much to scientific knowledge about North Dakota.[58]

A great nuisance to North Dakota farmers in the 1890s was smut in wheat, oats, and barley. The first bulletin describing this problem, titled "Grain Smuts," was published in 1891. This was the beginning of Bolley's work on the problem. For convenience smuts may be divided into loose or black smut of wheat, oats, and barley and stinking smut or bunt of wheat. Cereal crops develop smut as a result of one plant (smut fungi) growing on another (the infected crop). The black masses, known as smut, are countless smut spores (seeds). Farmers who sowed infected seed could lose 10 percent of the possible crop, or in the case of stinking smut as much as one-half to three-fourths of the crop. The trick was to destory the fungi in the seed wheat. A bulletin, "New Studies Upon the Smut of Wheat, Oats, and Barley" published in 1897, was based on Bolley's research and was important because it gave the standard formaldehyde (or Formalin, the trade name) treatment for the control of stinking smut in wheat.[59] Existing knowledge in 1897 led Bolley to enumerate four methods for treating wheat seed for smut—the corrosive sublimate method, the copper sulphate method, the hot water method, and the Formalin (formaldehyde) method. He described the Formalin treatment as saturating a large pile of grain with a solution of one pound of Formalin to 50 gallons of water. He advised that the pile should be shoveled over rapidly so that it should become thoroughly wet. The grain should be left in a pile for two to four hours, or else dipped for two hours.[60]

Bolley's work in treating smut was widely publicized. J.C. Walker, a pathologist with the University of Wisconsin, said of Bolley's formaldehyde treatment: "When Bolley initiated the use of formaldehyde, it became widely used especially upon oats, and is still about the cheapest method which is efficient."[61] Still, Bolley was tapping the same technological pool that other scientists were and the result was that some observers did not believe Bolley "initiated" that treatment. May Wood-Simons, writing for the *Technical World*, a predecessor of *Popular Mechanics*, believed that the credit for the formaldehyde treatment should go to the Wisconsin Experiment Station. She told the editor of *Technical World* that she based her beliefs on Wisconsin Station bulletins and interviews with knowledgeable farmers in Wisconsin. Her conclusion was that in Wisconsin, at least, the credit for the formaldehyde treatment for smut should go to the Wisconsin Station. A recent check with the Wisconsin Station reveals an earlier German report on formaldehyde treatment but no reports of experiments in the United States.[62] Such a qualification of Bolley's record, however, does not seriously detract from the originality of his research into the smut problem, no more than does possibly the earlier Japanese findings on flax wilt.

Wheat rust was another agricultural problem when Bolley arrived in Fargo in 1890. At Purdue he had already studied the problem of wheat rust and while there he published a bulletin in 1889 that defined the problem of wheat rust.[63] As early as 1865 DeBary was suggesting that barberry bushes were carriers of wheat rust spores. Although Bolley later took a strong stand for eradicating barberry bushes, he was not sure initially that the bushes were carriers of wheat rust spores.[64] "Certain it is the barberry is too rare a plant to be the cause of the widespread damage attributed to wheat rust," he wrote.[65] His earlier view of the relation of the barberry to grain rust epidemics changed with time. By 1906 he believed that barberry hedges contributed largely to rust epidemics. Since the bush was ornamental he believed substitutes could be found. Because of his agitation North Dakota enacted an eradication law in 1917 and in 1919 the USDA began cooperating with the state.[66]

Bolley's first publication on grain rust at Fargo was concerned with oat rust, rather than wheat rust. He reported on observations on the "variable susceptibility of different varieties of oats to attacks of rust" in 1894, 1895, and 1896. He believed at that time that the early white Russian variety was the most rust resistant. He did not state whether the oat rust he studied was stem or crown rust.[67]

In 1904 the North Dakota wheat crop was hit by black stem rust, giving Bolley an opportunity for extensive field work. Based on this work, he wrote about "Conditions which favor rust infection and destruction of the crop," as well as "what to do about wheat rust." He said farmers should improve drainage, they shoud sow good clean seed of high germinating qualities (at that time blue stem, the Fifes, and durum were the only available varieties), they should treat their seed for smut, and should control weed growth. In short, the farmer should practice good farming.[68]

Bolley's successful use of Darwin's survival of the fittest principle in flax selection for wilt-resistant flax led him to believe he could use the same methodology to achieve rust-resistant wheat. In 1911 his colleagues, J.A. Clark and L.R. Waldron, following in his footsteps, were testing samples of Kota, a wheat variety close in appearance to R.B.R.3, a Bolley selection from Europe. Later, Waldron crossed that selection with Marquis and produced the rust-resistant Ceres wheat, which entered into his breeding of other rust-resistant varieties--Rival, Vesta, and Mida. Waldron's greatness in plant breeding was partially the result, then, of the solid methodological foundations his teacher, Bolley, had laid down for him.[69]

Bolley's interest in chemical control of weeds dates from as early as 1896. By 1899 he was doing field tests with a solution of copper sulfate on weedy wheat. By 1900 he was experimenting with concentrations of sodium arsenite, sodium arsenate, copper sulphate, and salt.[70] In 1903 Bolley issued the first press bulletin, distributed to the rural press, on chemical destruction of weeds. By 1907 he was advocating chemicals for warding off the Canada thistle and using an iron sulphate solution in eradicating dandelions in lawns.[71] Bolley's most complete publication on chemical control of weeds was *Bulletin 80*, published in 1908.[72] He contributed many articles to the chemical trade press and farm journals regarding chemical control of weeds. The informative *Literary Digest* published an article about Bolley's theory that lawn dandelions could be destroyed by iron sulphate. The article created much interest, as did an article on the same subject in the important farm journal, the *Rural New Yorker*.[73]

Bolley rightly took great pride in his work on chemical control of weeds. But May Wood-Simons, writing in the *Technical World*, said she believed that the Wisconsin Experiment Station pioneered the use of iron sulphate to control weeds in the United States. She also thought that earlier tests in Germany had set a precedent for the Wisconsin experiments. The Wisconsin people had pointed out to her that there had been experiments in England and Scotland also. She closed her letter to the editor of the *Technical World*: "Having given credit to German authorities in the article, as the professor at Wisconsin Experiment Station also gives credit, I am unable to go further back in the discussion."[74] Records of the Wisconsin Experiment Station, however, show no earlier chemical treatment than Bolley's in the United States. None of the work done in Germany or at the Wisconsin Experiment Station really detracts from Bolley's work on technical control of weeds.

Bolley also made a pioneering contribution to North Dakota agriculture in his drive for legislation to assure pure seed. NDAC President Horace E. Stockbridge had mentioned the need for pure seed in his 1892 annual report, and Bolley, after publishing his first bulletin on wheat in 1893, brought out a bulletin on wheat seed the following year. Bolley had become convinced early that farming practices and seed quality in North Dakota were deplorable, believing that "if the wheat and flour products of North Dakota have a commercial standing of high standard, the credit is more justly to be assigned to the soil and atmospheric conditions than to farmer operations." He did praise North Dakota farmers for developing the farming frontier, but he charged that "there has been a miscellaneous use of indifferent, weedy, and disease-contaminated seed material throughout the state."[75] Such statements may have been good politics for enacting a pure seed law, but they were poor diplomacy. Bolley ended up offending both practicing farmers and conservatives interested in marketing farm mortgages in North Dakota. Yet in the long run he was an effective proponent of better seed.

Bolley was innovative in seeking new outlets for pure seed propaganda. Since Experiment Station bulletins and annual reports had poor circulation, he introduced press bulletins, which were sent out to the rural press and distributed at farmers' meetings.[76] The culmination of the propaganda effort by Bolley and others came in 1909 when the Legislature passed a pure seed law and made provisions for a commissioner to administer and supervise the law. The law was Senate Bill 119, introduced by Senator John J. Cashel, Democrat of Grafton. The director of the North Dakota Experiment Station was authorized by the law to appoint a pure seed commissioner and everyone assumed, rightly, that Bolley would get the job. The bill had had enthusiastic support in both houses and was signed by the governor. But it had been vigorously opposed by the American Seed Trade Association, and Dean H.L. Walster believed that only Bolley's fighting spirit had rescued the bill from oblivion. Bolley himself wrote to W.M. Hays of the Minnesota Station in 1909: "There has not been one minute since I put that seed bill in the North Dakota Legislature that it would not have been dead had I not staid (sic) on the ground." Bolley was appointed state seed commissioner in 1909, a position he held until 1929.[77] The law was amended in 1913 and in 1925 and the Office of State Seed Commisssioner was reorganized into a department in 1927.[78]

As state seed commissioner for 20 years, Bolley built up an effective seed test laboratory and an efficient body of field inspectors. In 1919 he wrote an article "Official Crop Inspection" that appeared in the prestigious journal *Science*. As the government demanded more and more production during World War I, Bolley feared that standards of purity might be brushed aside.[79] The seed program had always had opponents and Bolley in 1919 declared: "In years past we have gone so far in this *laissez faire* line on non-control of farming work, it (pure seed legislation) is sure to be resented by some lines of business, even though it meets with favor in the eyes of those for whom it is intended to directly help."[80] In thinking about farming, Bolley always put seed first. He believed that good seed would be followed by good farming methods. He wrote in the *Science* article in 1919: "When a farmer or wholesale seed merchant once becomes imbued with the idea of standardized seed of a known quality, sold under certification...he at once sees the necessity of following other processes of crop improvement which follow as natural corollaries."[81]

Always controversial, the appointment of a seed commissioner was up for grabs again in 1929. Because of friction in the Legislature, Bolley was given a two-year appointment instead of a longer term. Then on July 19, 1929, President John Lee Coulter was informed by the secretary of the Board of Administration that the Board had appointed E.M. Gillig as seed commissioner. Later in the month the secretary wrote to Coulter: "Probably some explanation should be made to you in regard to the appointment of Mr. Gillig as seed commissioner. This appointment was absolutely necessary as the state potato growers insisted that some man be appointed by the board who could give his entire time to the organization of this work.... Kindly extend to Professor Bolley the thanks of the board for the excellent service that he has rendered and assure him that the change was necessary, not from any lack of ambition on his part, but so that the seed commissioner would be entirely divorced from the faculty of the Agricultural College."[82]

Thus after 20 years of service, Bolley was replaced by a man who could "devote full time to the position." However, the appointment may have had political overtones as later in 1938 Governor Bill Langer tried to have Gillig named president of the Agricultural College instead of Dr. Frank Eversull.

Another of Bolley's research concerns was potato scab, which had caused economic loss to North Dakota farmers in the 1890s. While still quartered in Fargo College, Bolley isolated in his laboratory the fungus that caused potato scab. At the time he made photographs, drawings, and illustration of the potato scab, which produces a rough and pock-like condition on the surface of the tubers. Then on new land plowed out of the native buck brush, he planted in the spring of 1891 the first field of potatoes grown from intensely scabby seeds. He had treated these seeds by soaking the tubers in 1,200 mercuric chloride for one and one-half hours. Bolley's findings on the treatment were published in *Bulletin 4*, "Potato Scab and Possibilities of Prevention" in 1891. In the 1930s Bolley still stood by his methodology in the matter, although other methods had been developed at other experiment stations.[83]

Bolley took an early interest in soil conditions in virgin land. His experience with flax wilt led him to believe that diseases carried in the soil, not a loss of soil fertility, were behind deteriorating yields. One of his statements regarding wheat deterioration expressed this view: "Wheat deterioration in the fertile, wheat-growing areas of Northwest America involves soil and seed problems directly analogous to those in the flax crop or potato scab. It is not primarily a problem of soil fertility lost but of disease present."[84] Prescribing for that condition, Bolley recommended crop rotation, tillage, better seed selection, and good drainage.[85]

Bolley had been at the Agricultural College only about a year when a major public health problem confronted the people in the Red River the Valley of the North—typhoid fever. This disease was prevalent in the Valley in the 1890s and was sometimes called the Red River Fever. Bolley responded to a major outbreak in Grand Forks in the winter of 1893-94 by immediately making available information regarding the casual organism, Bacillus venosus, in *North Dakota Agricultural Experiment Station Bulletin 13*. In this publication, Bolley gave common-sense sanitary precautions. His primary suggestion was to boil drinking water. Bolley's researches regarding the water supply led him to wonder if milk, too, might be contaminated. He published findings regarding milk contamination in the prestigious *Proceedings of the Society for the Promotion of*

Agricultural Sciences in 1898.[86]

Bolley also did experiments regarding the efficacy of the widal or agglutination typhoid test that had been announced in Europe in 1856. His findings regarding the widal test were included in the eighth annual report of the North Dakota Agricultural Experiment Station in 1898.[87] Clearly, the botanist Bolley was also well trained in the new science of bacteriology.

In the early 1890s Bolley worked with his assistant trying to find an internal chemical cure for tree diseases, particularly apple blight and similar diseases. Tree feeding, either with chemicals or nutrients, was described by Bolley as "simply to bore a small hole into the body of the tree until the heartwood is reached. This is at once filled with water to exclude the air. Then a feeding flash or bottle is attached to the opening by a rubber or other close connection." He stated: "I am now firmly convinced that it is wholly within possibility to find a practical method of eliminating the destructive action of apple blight and many similar diseases. I do not say that the formaldehyde treatment here proposed will do this, but for three years it has appeared to give beneficial results with us against apple blight, plum pocket, sun-scald and sour-heart."[88] In spite of his conviction, results from tree feeding to cure tree diseases were mixed.[89]

A critical stage in Bolley's career was reached in 1911 when the Better Farming Association was organized following a bankers convention in Minneapolis. The convention was attended by bankers, lumbermen, and elevator owners from Minneapolis-St. Paul and North Dakota. NDAC President John Worst; E.J. Weiser, a prominent Fargo banker; and Alex Stern, Fargo businessman and Republican National Committeeman, were the Fargo delegation. The Better Farming Association was financed by Twin City interests and also had some support in North Dakota.[90] At this meeting and later, President Worst, Professor E.F. Ladd, and Bolley all came under attack, but the attack on Bolley became absolutely vitriolic. In later years President Worst summed up Bolley's work thusly: "Professor Bolley had solved the problem of preventing smut in wheat and other cereals, also found a remedy for potato scab, enunciated the cause of rust and produced a strain of flax highly resistant to flax wilt, if not positively immune to that disease. He also discovered the evident cause of the deterioration in the yield and quality of wheat—a fungus that causes the wheat roots to rot and is often referred to as 'root rot.'"[91]

With all those accomplishments benefiting North Dakota

farmers, the Better Farming Association still placed Bolley on its hit list. Bolley had made speeches and written bulletins exposing the diseased condition of the soil and the presence of rust, smut, flax-wilt, and potato scab in North Dakota. This aroused the ire of the association. Such talk, its members felt, would scare off eastern financiers who were furnishing mortgage money. Approximately 50 percent of North Dakota farms were mortgaged by 1910. Local bankers were receiving eastern money at six percent and were loaning the money out at ten percent, and they would oppose anyone who threatened this lucrative situation. Realtors and bankers were convinced that Bolley's research that showed flax and wheat disease were soil-borne would reduce farmland values.[92]

President Worst defended Bolley against these attacks, thereby increasing the pressure on his own position. On one occasion President Worst was befriending Bolley when a member of the Board of Trustees broke into the discussion with a bitter tirade against Bolley. He indicated that Bolley had done more to discredit the state than any other man. Then another member of the Board summed up: "The State could better afford to pay Bolley $25,000 a year to get out of the state or keep his d____d mouth shut."[93]

Bolley's position was made even more untenable by the appointment of the arch conservative Thomas Cooper by the College Board of Trustees to replace President Worst as director of the Experiment Station in 1914. Cooper was a native of Illinois and a recent graduate of the University of Minnesota. The appointment placed both Bolley and Ladd under Cooper's jurisdiction and Cooper soon made it clear that both Bolley and Ladd would have to be more conservative in their findings. Ladd refused to accept this change and continued his pure food and drug and flour milling experiments on his own.[94] Bolley apparently resolved to hold down his position and resist Cooper's encroachment on his work. In 1915 Cooper refused to allow the publication of a Bolley circular titled "Deterioration of Durum Wheat—Head and Root Blighting, Admixtures." Bolley angrily protested, saying he would not consent to censorship on Cooper's part.[95] By 1916 Bolley was corresponding with M.L. Wilson of Montana State College and Station regarding Cooper's motivation in coming to North Dakota. Wilson seems to have felt that Cooper's job was to "get" Worst, Bolley and Ladd for the Better Farming Association. Bolley also asked Wilson to give him information concerning the original Better Farming Association meeting in Minneapolis. Apparently Wilson was less helpful than Bolley had hoped.[96]

Worst was forced out of office by 1916, but the Board of Trustees elected Professor Ladd to replace him. Ladd was too universally admired to be let out and his qualifications made him the right man for the job. Thomas Cooper remained as director of the Experiment Station and Extension until 1917. With his old foe Ladd at the helm Cooper's position had become untenable.

After Ladd became president of the Agricultural College, two assistants in botany, D.G. Milbraith and W.H. Mercer, brought charges of unprofessional acts against Bolley. President Ladd appointed a committee consisting of Dean of Mechanic Arts E.S. Keene, Dr. Leunis Van Es, who later became acting director of the Experiment Station, and Dean of Agriculture C.B. Waldron to hear the charges. Their findings were sent to the Board of Trustees and a board subcommittee visited the campus. The two accusers were dismissed, but they received recommendations stating that they were competent. One result of the hearing of 1916 was that the NDAC faculty organized a chapter of the American Federation of Teachers. One of this group's functions was to protect faculty from unfair personnel practices but it did not insist on the right to strike.[97]

As a part of his investigation of Bolley, Dean Keene sent out a circular letter inquiring about Bolley's standing as a scientist and asking for evaluations of his character. A former student of Bolley's, Thomas Mann, wrote: "I have kept in very close touch with the work that Professor Bolley has been doing, and I consider his investigations very accurate; he is probably a decade or two in advance of his fellow workers." He added that he had spent three years with Bolley on flax problems.[98] Another student, Daniel J. Glomset, M.D., declared: "What little I may have accomplished in scientific medicine I owe largely to the scientific principles and enthusiasm which were instilled into me by Professor Bolley during the years that I worked in his department."[99]

Bolley's alma mater, Purdue, rated him highly. Director of the Experiment Station Arthur Goss wrote: "Professor Bolley was located for several years at the Indiana Station; while here, he did some of the best research work the Indiana Station has ever turned out."[100]

Bolley also received praise from Cornell in a letter from plant pathologist H.H. Whitzel. Whitzel declared: "It is with surprise and deep concern that I read such a request for an opinion of my colleague, Dr. H.L. Bolley; surprise that there should be any question as to his scientific integrity, concern that any man or body of men should attempt to discredit a reputation built upon a lifetime of notable labors and unselfish devotion to the science of agriculture."[101]

E.M. East, Harvard biologist, stated that the entire problem was caused by politics. He wrote: "Bolley's attainments have been questioned for political reasons, and I suspect that those who are behind the matter have reasons similar to those food adulterators who work for the removal of Dr. (Harvey) Wiley of Washington."[102] Professor East was certainly accurate in his diagnosis.

Bolley's personal characteristics also received comment in the investigation. L.R. Jones, plant pathologist at Wisconsin, declared: "Bolley has (been) by a combination of originality bordering on what we sometimes term 'genius,' and persistent study of agricultural practices,...peculiarly successful in devising and applying new remedial measures."[103] W.G. Farlow, Harvard botanist, said: "In his case he (Bolley) is by nature what is generally described as 'intense.'"[104] C.S. Plumb, animal husbandryman at Ohio State University, wrote concerning Bolley: "I have always known that Professor Bolley was somewhat peculiar in his characteristics, but this is the first time that I have ever heard any question raised as to his scientific standing."[105] C.M. Piper, botanist and agronomist of the USDA, declared: "You have in Professor Bolley a man of most unusual ability whose eccentricities and over-enthusiasm can be so easily guarded against that it would be a very serious mistake to permit adverse criticism to militate against him." Years later Bolley's contemporaries would define his being eccentric as a trait of individualism, coupled with quick wittedness, and possibly secretiveness about his own work.[106] All in all, Bolley received good marks from the scientists polled. If he was a little individualistic, they were willing to put up with that.

The North Dakota Seed Law, which Bolley had supported, came under attack in the survey. F.C. Steward, plant pathologist of the New York Experiment Station, summed up the opposition to the Seed Law when he wrote: "Concerning the Seed Law I will say that I consider it too complex and too drastic."[107] Stewart's director concurred in that opinion, as did E.A. Burnett, agriculturalist of the Nebraska College of Agriculture.[108] But letters criticizing the North Dakota Seed Law were in the minority in the poll. The results of Dean Keene's survey were largely what one would expect in view of Bolley's background.

Bolley had been trained in biological science by J.C. Arthur, who came to Purdue in 1887 carrying with him the seed of the "new botany." Bolley was one of his early and enthusiastic students. In Arthur's biography the name of Bolley heads the list of botanists heavily influenced by him. The two men carried on a fruitful correspondence for many years, with their letters dealing mainly with Arthur's specialty, the rusts.[109] A researcher at the Connecticut Experiment Station, in a 1915 address titled "Botany in Relation to Agriculture," paid special attention to Bolley's flax work, his work with L.R. Waldron on classification of plants, and his contribution in potato scab research.[110] These people appreciated his work.

Bolley, then, brought with him to Fargo both his youthful enthusiasm and the research tools of the new botany. In some cases, such as the rusts, he carried on in the tradition of his mentor. Still, he blazed new paths in flax-wilt research, the use of formaldehyde treatment for smuts of grain, chemical destruction of weeds, crusade for pure seed, common potato scab research, his interest in tree feeding, and in trying to solve the problem of typhoid in water and milk.

Some of his original researches were duplicated. Japanese scientists had been working on the flax-wilt problem before Bolley, and Wisconsin agri-scientists may have predated Bolley in the formaldehyde treatment for smuts of grain and chemical spraying for weeds. The best evidence, though, indicates that Bolley introduced these procedures in the United States. The fact that others were carrying on similar research in no way detracts from Bolley's contribution to agricultural science or his great efforts on behalf of North Dakota and North Dakota farmers. What it does indicate is that there was a great body of technical and scientific knowledge being accumulated in the 19th and 20th centuries and anyone who had the proper training, who kept up with the literature, and who could make the applications could tap that pool. Therefore, there were often simultaneous discoveries in different places.

Bolley was far more than an experiment station researcher. He was a valued member of the instructional faculty and he contributed significantly to student life when he introduced football at the Agricultural College and helped instigate the natural rivalry between NDAC and the University. Aggie fans have never stopped exulting over the first year's victory over the University. Football took firm root in the new northwest and was soon played there as enthusiastically as if it were native to the region. Bolley was the man behind the institutionalization of football in North Dakota.

His contributions were very significant. Perhaps a story told by the late W.C. Hunter in *Beacon Across the Prairie* will sum them up. He related a talk with a farmer concerning Bolley: "Could any man be worth a hundred thousand dollars? Yes, said the farmer, it was possible that a man might be worth that much. Could a man be worth five hundred thousand dollars? The farmer was not sure, but conceded that there might be a few such men. Could a man be valued at a million dollars? Well, replied the farmer, he knew of only one man who could possibly be worth a million dollars— and that was Professor Bolley down at the Agricultural College— he was easily worth a million dollars to North Dakota alone!"[111]

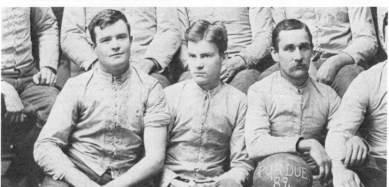

Henry Bolley was the first NDAC football coach (above) and an
ardent Bison football fan throughout his life. He quarterbacked at
Purdue in 1889 (front row, center).

In 1903 Bolley was commissioned by the federal government to visit Europe and Russia to acquire seeds of plant varieties to be bred in the U.S.

In the 1930s the USDA estimated the value of the flax seed bred by
Henry Bolley at $37 million.

For more than 40 consecutive years Henry Bolley planted flax on the same eighth of an acre at Plot 30 in order to produce the hardiest strain of flax possible. The experiment at Plot 30 has been continued by Bolley's successors and is now nearly a century old.

Footnotes

[1]The best overall sketch of Bolley was written by himself. See Bolley to Tracy W. Johnson, Publications Department, North Dakota Agricultural College, in the Henry Luke Bolley Papers, North Dakota Institute for Regional Studies. The best biography of Bolley is H.L. Walster, "Henry Luke Bolley, A Biography of a Man of Science" in *Five for the Land,* unpublished manuscript in NDIRS.

[2]Sketch prepared by Henry Luke Bolley for the *Fargo Forum,* February 18, 1934, Bolley papers, NDIRS.

[3]*Ibid.*

[4]Bolley to J.E. Balfour, 6 Carmelite Street, London (Burke's *Landed Gentry,)* June 10, 1937, Bolley papers, NDIRS.

[5]Sketch, NDIRS.

[6]Walster, "Henry Luke Bolley," NDIRS, p. 1.

[7]"Henry Luke Bolley, M.S., Professor of Botany and Zoology," *The Spectrum,* Vol. II No. 8, May 1898, p. 2.

[8]Walster, "Henry Luke Bolley," NDIRS, p. 1.

[9]W.G. Farlow, Harvard, "The Change from the Old to the New Botany in the United States," *Science,* Vol. 37, (1913), pp. 79-81.

[10]Frank D. Kern, "Joseph Charles Arthur, 1850-1942," *Phutopathology,* Vol. 32, No. 10, October 1942, pp. 834-836.

[11]Henry Luke Bolley, "Early Days at the A.C.," *College and State,* November 1923, p. 11.

[12]"Henry L. Bolley, M.S., Professor of Botany and Zoology," *The Spectrum,* Vol. II, No. 8, May 1898, p. 2.

[13]Henry Luke Bolley, "Early Days at the A.C.," *College and State,* November 1923, p. 11.

[14]*Ibid.*

[15]Bolley to Tracy W. Johnson, Bolley Papers, NDIRS, pp. 1-2.

[16]Henry Luke Bolley, "Early Days at the A.C.," *College and State,* November 1923, p. 11.

[17]Bolley to Johnson, Bolley Papers, NDIRS, p. 2.

[18]*Ibid.*, p. 2. Hunter in *Beacon Across the Prairie,* p. 19, tells the same Edwards story.

[19]*Ibid.*, pp. 2-3.

[20]Henry Luke Bolley, "Football at the North Dakota Agricultural College," December 16, 1933, Bolley Papers, NDIRS, p. 1.

[21]*Ibid,* pp. 1-2.

[22]K.W. Greene, "Football at A.C. Thirty Years Ago," *College and State,* VI, No. 1, 1922, p. 7.

[23]*Ibid.*, p. 6.

[24]*Ibid.*

[25]*Ibid.*

[26]*Ibid.*

[27]*Ibid.*

[28]*Ibid.*

[29]*Ibid.*, p. 2.

[30]*Ibid.*

[31]*Ibid.*

[32]*The Spectrum,*Vol. 5, No. 1, October 15, 1900.

[33]K.W. Greene, "Football at North Dakota Agricultural College."

[34]Hunter, *Beacon,* p. 27.

[35]*Ibid.* For Miss Sheldon's position at Fargo College consult Bill G. Reid, "The North Dakota Votes for Women League - Fargo Branch: Vital Reform or Disappointing Failure?" in Institute Room, Library.

[36]Bolley to J.E. Balfour, London, Burke's *Landed Gentry,* June 10, 1937.

[37]*Ibid.*

[38]Bolley to Professor L.R. Jones, Burlington, Vermont, October 23, 1901, Bolley Papers, NDIRS.

[39]*Ibid.*

[40]*Ibid.*

[41]*Ibid.* Science Hall was later renamed Minard Hall.

[42]*Ibid.*

[43]*Ibid.*

[44]Walster, "Henry Luke Bolley," NDIR, p. 6.

[45]A.C. Dillman, "Improvement in Flax," USDA. *Yearbook,* 1936, pp. 748-749.

[46]*Ibid.*, p. 7.

[47]Kingo Muyabe, Sapporo Agricultural College, Sapporo, Japan, September 25, 1902, Bolley Papers, NDIRS.

[48]Kingo Muyabe, Sapporo Agricultural College, Sapporo, Japan, to Bolley, December 5, 1902, Bolley Papers, NDIRS.

[49]Walster, "Henry Luke Bolley," pp. 19-20.

[50]*Ibid.* p. 22.

[51]*Ibid.*, p. 20. See also H.L. Bolley and J.J. Pritchard, *Rust Problems: Facts, Observations and Theories, Possible Means of Control* (Fargo: Agricultural College, Department of Botany, 1906), pp. 614-618, 619-654.

[52]*Ibid.*

[53]H.L. Bolley, *Flax Culture,* Bulletin No. 71, North Dakota Experiment Station, 1906.

[54]Correspondent Unknown, USDA to Bolley, April 13, 1906, Bolley Papers, NDIRS.

[55]Walster, "Henry Luke Bolley" p. 21. See Bulletin 71.

[56]"College Assigns Bolley to South America Study," *College and State,* December 1929, p. 11.

[57]Walster, "Henry Luke Bolley," pp. 24-26. Bolley's flax varieties were almost endless. They included: Brida, Bison, Victory, Bolley Golden, Smoky Golden, Rio, and B-5128. Bulletin #71, p. 144.

⁵⁸O.A. Stevens, *Handbook of North Dakota Plants*, (Fargo: NDIRS, 1963), p. 3.

⁵⁹Bolley to Tracy W. Johnson, Publications Department, "A-C," November 11, 1934, Bolley Papers, NDIRS, pp. 3-4. See also Henry Luke Bolley, Bulletin #1 *Grain Smuts, 1891*, and same author, Bulletin 27, *New Studies Upon the Smut of Wheat, Oats and Barley, 1897*.

⁶⁰Walster, "Henry Luke Bolley," pp. 47-48, Bolley papers, NDIRS.

⁶¹*Ibid.*, p. 48.

⁶²May Wood-Simons to editor of the *Technical World*, Bolley Papers, NDIRS. See Drace C. Army, Plant Pathologist, University of Wisconsin-Madison, to writer, April 15, 1982.

⁶³Walster, "Henry Luke Bolley," Bolley Papers, NDIRS, p. 53 H.L. Bolley, "Wheat Rust," Indiana Experiment Station, 1889.

⁶⁴*Ibid.*, p. 54.

⁶⁵*Ibid.*

⁶⁶*Ibid.*

⁶⁷*Ibid.*

⁶⁸*Ibid.*, pp. 55, 57.

⁶⁹*Ibid.*, pp. 58-62 and p. 54.

⁷⁰*Ibid.*, pp. 103-104. See also "Killing Weeds by Spraying," *Literary Digest*, July 31, 1909.

⁷¹*Ibid.*, pp. 104-105.

⁷²*Ibid.*, p. 106.

⁷³*Ibid.*, p. 107. See also "Killing Weeds by Spraying," *Literary Digest*, July 31, 1909.

⁷⁴May Wood-Simons to editor of the *Technical World*, Bolley Papers, NDIRS.

⁷⁵Walster, "Henry Luke Bolley," Bolley Papers, NDIRS, pp. 114-115.

⁷⁶*Ibid.*, p. 116

⁷⁷*Ibid.*, pp. 116-117. See also Hunter, *Beacon Across the Prairie*, p. 47.

⁷⁸*Ibid.*, p. 118.

⁷⁹*Ibid.*, pp. 118-119. See also H.L. Bolley, "Official Field Crop Inspection," August 19, 1919, pp. 193-199.

⁸⁰Bolley, "Official Field Crop Inspection," p. 195.

⁸¹*Ibid.*, p. 199.

⁸²Hunter, *Beacon Across the Prairie*, pp. 124-125.

⁸³Bolley to Tracy W. Johnson, Publications Department, "A-C," November 11, 1934, Bolley Papers, NDIRS. See also Walster, "Henry Luke Bolley," NDIRS, p. 78, and H.L. Bolley "Potato Scab and Possibilities of Prevention," Bulletin #4, North Dakota Experiment Station, p. 3.

⁸⁴Walster, "Henry Luke Bolley," Bolley Papers, NDIRS, p. 84.

⁸⁵*Ibid.*, p. 85.

⁸⁶*Ibid.*, pp. 121a-121b.

⁸⁷*Ibid.*, p. 121c.

⁸⁸*Ibid.*, pp. 123, 125.

⁸⁹*Ibid.*, pp. 123-125.

[90]Hunter, *Beacon Across the Prairie,* p. 58.

[91]J.H. Worst (?), "The Looting of the North Dakota Agricultural College, some inside history," Bolley papers, NDIRS, pp. 2-3. This article is evidently the work of Worst.

[92]Hunter, *Beacon Across the Prairie,* pp. 58-59.

[93]Worst, "Looting of the A.C.," p. 7.

[94]Hunter, *Beacon Across the Prairie,* p. 61

[95]Bolley to Thomas Cooper, September 2, 1915, Bolley papers, NDIRS.

[96]Bolley letters to M.L. Wilson, January 25, 1916, and February 7, 1916, Bolley Papers, NDIRS.

[97]Hunter, *Beacon Across the Prairie,* p. 91.

[98]Thomas F. Mann, Delaware College Experiment Station, to Keene, June 24, 1916, Bolley Papers, NDIRS.

[99]Daniel J. Glomset, M.D., Des Moines, Iowa, to Keene, June 24, 1916. Bolley papers, NDIRS.

[100]Arthur Goss, Purdue, to Keene, June 22, 1916, Bolley Papers, NDIRS.

[101]H.H. Whitzel to Keene, June 24, 1916, Bolley Papers, NDIRS.

[102]E.M. East to Keene, June 28, 1916, Bolley Papers, NDIRS.

[103]L.R. Jones to Keene, June 24, 1916, Bolley Papers, NDIRS.

[104]W.G. Farlow to Keene, June 24, 1916, Bolley Papers, NDIRS.

[105]C.S. Plumb to Keene, June 23, 1916, Bolley Papers, NDIRS. Interview with Theodore E. Stoa, March 29, 1982.

[106]C.M. Piper to Keene, June 26, 1916, Bolley Papers, NDIRS.

[107]F.C. Stewart to Keene, June 23, 1916, Bolley Papers, NDIRS.

[108]W.H. Jordan to Keene, June 24, 1916, and E.A. Burnett to Keene, June 24, 1916, Bolley Papers, NDIRS.

[109]Walster, "Henry Luke Bolley," Bolley Papers, NDIRS, p. 127.

[110]*Ibid.,* p. 129.

[111]Hunter, *Beacon Across the Prairie,* p. 47.

Edwin Fremont Ladd

Edwin Fremont Ladd, Scientist as Pure Food Crusader, College Administrator and U.S. Senator

Edwin Fremont Ladd was born December 13, 1859, in a rural community outside of Starkes, Maine, a small crossroads town with a post office, general store, and a number of churches.[1] The Ladd family was lineage-proud in the New England sense and maintained it could trace its family line to 650 A.D. and the "Earl of Lad" in Norway. According to family records, the Ladd family later emigrated to Normandy and England. The first Ladd in the New World was Daniel of Ipswich, Massachusetts, who arrived in 1634[2] and who was to have many descendants scattered throughout New England and the Old Northwest.

Edwin Ladd's childhood was typical of farm youth of the time. In addition to other farm enterprises, the family apparently experimented with purebred Herefords during his youth. Of his parents, his mother probably had the most impact on Ladd. She was characterized as "a stern, small, very sturdy lady."[3] Something can be ascertained concerning the political and moral philosophy of Ladd's parents by the fact that his middle name was Fremont, probably for John C. Fremont, the first Republican and anti-slavery candidate for president.[4]

Ladd's formal education was considerably above the national average for the late 19th century. He was educated in the Maine public schools, at Somerset Academy in Athens, Maine, and at the University of Maine, from which he graduated in 1884.[5] While at the University he first enrolled in the science and literature curriculum, but finding that not to his taste he switched to agriculture courses. While there he took courses that gave him a good scientific background, but he also obtained a broad liberal arts foundation.[6] Ladd's work brought him no special honors, but his performance was above average for his class.[7] While at the University he was a member of the QTV fraternity and was a lieutenant in the Coburn Cadets. He sported a beard when he graduated from college, as did all the male members of his class.[8] While at the University he studied chemistry under Professor Alfred Aubert, whose specialty was picolins compounds, a derivative of coal tar to be used to produce drugs and dyes."[9] He would make good use of Aubert's speciality after he graduated from the University in 1884.

After his college years Ladd was employed as a chemist by the New York Experiment Station at Geneva.[10] He was still very young and he seemed to have had a preference for becoming a physician, but his five years at the New York Experiment Station confirmed him as a chemist.[11] During these years Ladd undoubtedly was influenced by working under Stephen Babcock, a man who was to become known as the inventor of the Babcock test for ascertaining the butterfat content of milk. After Babcock left to go to the Wisconsin Station, Ladd became chief chemist at Geneva. Typical of agricultural chemists in the latter part of the 19th century, Ladd was concerned with fertilizer problems while at Geneva. Station Director E. Lewis Sturtevant spoke well of Ladd, writing: "The work of our Assistant Chemist upon artificial digestion of fodders, and also his investigation upon the action of phosphoric acid in fertilizers deserves special notice."[12]

In his last year at the Station Ladd seems to have become restive. He had made plans to establish a commercial laboratory in New York City in the summer of 1890.[13] But at about the same time, he received an offer from North Dakota Agricultural College to become an instructor of chemistry at the College as well as chief chemist for the Experiment Station attached to the College. Why he accepted the offer is difficult to understand. North Dakota in 1890 was one year into statehood, the Indian Wars were still an echo, and the state was poorly developed. Perhaps he was influenced by Stephen Babcock's advice that a young man could find opportunity in the west[14] or perhaps he wanted a regular paycheck, as opposed to a risky business venture.

When Ladd arrived in Fargo he found the new school without a physical plant and with only a rudimentary staff. He joined the young faculty in holding classes in the basement of Fargo College. One of the original faculty, H.L. Bolley, recalled that Ladd immediately became a power in the infant institution with his insistence upon the "finest degree of scientific exactness" and making the work "applicable to the need of the people." Probably without knowing it Ladd was describing the land grant philosophy of education at its best. In 1890 Ladd still had a boyish appearance in spite of his full beard. He was short, had blond hair, blue eyes, and even features. He was overly serious and quick to anger. His sprightly walk testified that he was a busy man. His high tenor voice tended to be a distracting factor in his teaching and even in his later administrative and political career.[15]

The name Ladd soon became synonymous with the chemistry program at North Dakota Agricultural College. When College Hall (later Old Main) was completed in 1891 he taught chemistry, nutrition, paints, cereal chemistry, and dairy products in the basement of that building. He also taught grammar and, on one occasion, laid down an ultimatum to the president that he had to have an unabridged dictionary if he were to continue. He got the dictionary. In the early days Ladd taught short courses, as did the other faculty. In his case they dealt with principles of chemistry, balanced rations, nutritive ratio, and dairy products. Ladd's teaching has been referred to as "unimaginative," but his students graduated to compete with those of older, larger schools.[16] Even as the Chemistry Department expanded, Ladd remained its guiding light until he became president of the College in 1916.[17] During this period the chemistry program included pharmacy, nutrition, agricultural biochemistry, and the State Testing Laboratory.[18]

Ladd early built up good relations with his colleagues, both in Fargo and throughout the state. He was a friend and associate of chemist George Alonzo Abbott of the University of North Dakota, although Abbott felt that Ladd was "obsessed with an analytical approach to chemistry" which "limited his field of inquiry." William Tudor Pearce, who later became dean of the School of Chemistry at NDAC, was his friend and colleague, and Ladd was a close collaborator with John Henry Shepperd, who later also became president of the Agricultural College.[19]

Along with his work in the Chemistry Department, Ladd became interested in the kinds of paints that would endure in the harsh climate of the Northern Great Plains. This interest was thrust upon him as the North Dakota Legislature passed a comprehensive paint law in 1905 that made the Experiment Station responsible for the quality of paints sold in the state. Paint manufacturers were at first dubious about the law, filing suit questioning its constitutionality, but Judge Charles F. Amidon of the U.S. District Court in Fargo declared the law constitutional in 1906. Ladd's paint experiments were soon known all over the state. Extensive paint experiments began in 1906 when the first paint fence was erected. Soon he had many more fences erected on campus and was carrying out tests on private residences and public buildings. These experiments were of interest to North Dakotans since they grew flax seed that contained linseed oil used in making paint. They also purchased paint for their buildings, which were mainly wooden. After the initial apathy, the Paint Manufacturers Association of the

United States and the National Lead Company cooperated heartily with Ladd, and he received funds from paint men who had "clubbed together" for that purpose. From his findings manufacturers learned useful things and consumers received a better paint product. To the present day, Ladd's work endures at North Dakota State University with its outstanding Department of Polymers and Coatings.[20]

Ladd's early years at the Agricultural College and Station were busy and productive. Almost immediately he led the way to the creation of a North Dakota Dairy Association. In a developing state with a one- or two-crop economy Ladd undoubtedly felt that diversification was needed to secure a stable economic base for North Dakota farmers.[21] His interest in dairying was taken up by the College as early as 1896.

In early days, Ladd also performed analysis of various substances for North Dakota residents, testing, among other things, water, cider and vinegar, and other substances for alcohol content. From these early tests he was laying the groundwork for his later interest in adulteration of food and other products.[22] He also did soil analysis. In those early years this consisted of treating a weighed soil sample with hydrochloric (muriatic) acid and then analyzing the dissolved substance for the several elements. By 1892 he had formed opinions from these tests concerning wheat growing potential and the possibilities of dairying in North Dakota. He wrote that year: "So productive is the soil of North Dakota that many consider it inexhaustible—this is not true." He noted that history proves that crop rotation and fertilization are necessary for successful farming. In 1900 he told the Tri-State Grain Growers at Fargo: "It is not fertility that our soil lacks, that is, fertility in the sense of phosphoric acid, potash and even for the present nitrogen, but rather a keeping up of the stock of organic matter to be gradually converted into humus." To achieve this goal he strongly recommended a seven-year crop rotation.[23]

While Ladd was busy creating new dimensions for the Experiment Station, he was applying this same energy to his social life and enjoyed equal success. In 1891 he was busily engaged in having a summer cottage built for himself and other professors at Detroit Lakes, Minnesota.[24] Ladd developed early friendships on the south side of Fargo that resulted in his meeting Rizpah Sprogle of Annapolis, Maryland, at a tennis party when Miss Sprogle was visiting a childhood friend. Ladd and she were married August 10, 1893, in Annapolis. "For Ladd it was a fortunate choice. While he was outspoken and stern, she was tactful. She invested her surroundings with a charm and grace that made the Ladd home a favorite of students and acquaintances. When he offended friends with his frankness, as he occasionally did, she would intercede for him. He had little talent for apology." The Ladds established their home at 1104 13th Street North in Fargo where they raised eight children—Edwin Fremont Jr., E. Vernon, Culver, D. Milton, Rizpah and Rosilla (twins), Katherine, and Elizabeth. Ladd's favorite pastime was his garden, although he continued playing tennis and at one time hunted bison.[25] The Ladds were amiable and sociable to a marked degree. W.C. Hunter, North Dakota State University historian, related that Mrs. Ladd often stationed one of the children at a window to see who "Pappa" was bringing home to dinner.[26] H.L. Walster remembered the Ladds' hospitality thus: "I can see him now, in my mind's eye, standing at the head of the table, for he was a short man, carving a holiday roast for his family and several fortunate holiday guests."[27]

In addition to their personal sociability, the Ladds were active in Fargo community affairs. They were active in the First Presbyterian Church of Fargo and Ladd served as a trustee of the church. He also served on the Fargo Board of Education for several years.[28] As a matter of fact, all the faculty of the young Agricultural College were active in the affairs of the young and growing Fargo[29] and in that way Ladd was representative of the faculty.

Of all his activities, however, none is so vital to an understanding of Ladd as his work in the pure food crusade. North Dakotans have been fond of pointing out that North Dakota's pure food law dates from July 1, 1903, while the federal law wasn't passed until 1906. From this North Dakotans have assumed that Ladd had a good deal of influence in the national pure food movement, and they have more or less equated him with the famous Dr. Harvey W. Wiley of the Division of Chemistry of the United States Department of Agriculture.[30] More correctly, as Wiley's biographer asserts, both the local laws and the national legislation were part of the progressive urge for reform that swept the nation after the turn of the century.[31] Local conditions on the pure food front had been bad. Ladd wrote: "From personal experience I know that from 1890-1902 North Dakota was a veritable dumping-ground for the waste food products to be found in the United States." The North Dakota Pure Food Act called for the chemist of the Station, Ladd, to be named food commissioner and to enforce the law, and it provided an appropriation of $1,500.[32]

In his new position, Ladd confronted a number of problems.

He wrote later: "Do you know that for more than two years I did not go to bed a single night without a libel suit or an injunction, or both, hanging over my head, and knowing that on the morrow I must be preparing for my defense?" Manufacturers shipped their goods into the state under federal interstate commerce laws, thus Ladd could only reach the retailers of the products on the state level. Still, he had a number of advantages. Much of Ladd's success in North Dakota can be attributed to the almost complete support he received from state and federal judges. Charles A. Pollock of the state court and Charles F. Amidon of the federal court both ruled in his favor. As a matter of fact, the Amidons and Ladds socialized together. Much of Ladd's success, too, can be attributed to the lack of food manufacturing in North Dakota. No politician had constituents who were hurt by Ladd's rulings. Pure food crusaders in other states were not treated so tenderly. In a 1904 letter, Food Commissioner William McConnell of Minnesota wrote Ladd of his frustration with his state courts. In Pennsylvania, Missouri, and South Dakota, court rulings almost brought the pure food movement to a standstill. Only when Ladd ruled against the Alsop process, which was used by some North Dakota millers in bleaching flour, did he temporarily get into trouble.[33]

Ladd believed firmly in the effectiveness of publicity, and in 1899, together with "Uncle Will" Crocker of Lisbon, he began publishing his own farm journal.[34] The journal first appeared under the title *The Sanitary Home*, and its publishers announced it would be popular, "scientific in spirit, but not technical."[35] After four years the journal became known as *The North Dakota Farmer and Sanitary Home*. In 1904 it became simply *The North Dakota Farmer*, although it still carried articles relative to the home.[36] With his own journal reaching farmers, Ladd had little difficulty swaying public opinion to his side. His ultimate weapon, of course, was his official position with the Agricultural College and the Experiment Station. This connection, in a state where the College and Station had rendered direct service to farmers, had an important bearing on the pure food program's success.

Within six months after the Pure Food Law was passed, Ladd was able to report a noticeable improvement in the quality of goods shipped into the state.[37] He believed that with the exception of three or four large out-of-state shippers everyone had manifested a desire to have goods in shape to meet the approval of his department.[38]

As food commissioner, Ladd set out early to establish guidelines for producers. He declared that harmful chemical preservatives were not to be used in food products or beverages. He prohibited coloring matters that would tend to deceive purchasers, such colorings being considered adulterants. Ladd also wanted all food products labeled, as inferior products used as substitutes were considered adulterants. Finally, Ladd relied on Dr. Harvey Wiley of the USDA for guidance in determining what chemical preservatives were unsafe for consumption.[39] Ladd attempted to be reasonable in his rulings. He once quipped: "The pure food law does not prohibit the selling of ground olive stones or coconut shells as such, but it does forbid selling them for peppers or other food products.[40]

Several of Ladd's rulings led to court battles and he sometimes found himself facing the wrath of an entire industry. One was the particularly bitter dispute over ketchup. Some manufacturers claimed ketchup would spoil without chemical preservatives and backed this up by quoting government experts on the question. Ladd checked with his own government official and found at least one manufacturer was shipping ketchup into the state without preservatives, except those with condimental properties, so he continued to enforce his original rulings concerning chemical preservatives and ketchup.[41]

In another situation, Ladd found himself protecting the interests of North Dakota wheat farmers involving a dispute over bleached flour. A certain type of North Dakota wheat produced a very white flour and this wheat brought a premium price. However, millers soon developed methods to bleach out other wheat varieties and started substituting them for the North Dakota wheat. The controversy swirled all the way to the USDA and the U.S. Supreme Court, and Ladd even testified about bleached flour in England. He wanted to ban the sale of bleached flour in North Dakota, but under North Dakota law the best he could do was to require bleached flour be labeled as such. Even then, millers could mix the North Dakota wheat with other wheat products to get around the law.[42]

Ladd's interest in the welfare of North Dakota farmers often went beyond enforcing pure food laws. In 1907 he had an experimental mill built on the college campus. This mill was intended to determine the value of North Dakota wheat as to yield, protein value, quality of flour, and quality of bread. He found that a surprisingly good quality of flour could be made from light wheat, even that damaged by rust epidemics. This finding had particular importance in 1916 when hot winds shrivelled the kernels of the North Dakota wheat crop and it was also hit by rust. Millers in

Minneapolis and Duluth said the crop was only good for chicken feed and they established a grading system of A, B, C, and D whereby farmers lost 40 cent to $1.05 per bushel if their wheat was rated at a lower grade. Then Minneapolis millers had "the supreme audacity to claim superior quality for this flour (made from the shrivelled kernels) on the ground that it was unusually rich in gluten—that is, it absorbed a large amount (of) water and made an exceptionally large loaf of bread." Circulars sent to the trade came into Ladd's hands, and he exposed the swindle. He said: "It was this fact more than any other which caused the farmers of North Dakota to enroll in the Nonpartisan League in such numbers." The "AC Mill," as the campus experimental mill was called, was used for the USDA in establishing milling grades that helped end pricing abuses. Such grading was probably Ladd's greatest contribution to the North Dakota farmer. In another instance of the mill's use, the well-known wheat variety Ceres went through milling and baking tests before it was distributed to farmers. The AC Mill was one of the antecedents of the Department of Cereal Chemistry and Technology at North Dakota State University.

Ladd also addressed the U.S Senate on rust and the barberry bush. He expressed the view that barberry eradication was really a federal problem.[43]

Cerealist M.A. Carleton of the USDA was stimulating interest in durum wheat at the turn of the century. He declared that in Eastern Russia, "Kubankas, the chief macaroni variety, is the most popular for making bread in that region." He also hailed durum as the best wheat for the semi-arid plains. With this sort of prestigious propaganda emanating from the USDA it is not surprising that Ladd devoted considerable time to durum research.[44]

Ladd wrote a very strong article in the *North Dakota Farmer* in 1908 urging the use of durum as a bread wheat. If it could be used for bread, he felt it should not be downgraded so much in price. He also noted that it should not be grown in the Red River Valley as the moisture there caused it to deteriorate. He is never quoted as advocating the use of durum in making semolina from which macaroni and similar alimentary pastes are made. Ladd's conclusions were wrong; durum is not suitable as a bread wheat. It has, though, won a place in North Dakota as a macaroni wheat and in some years North Dakota produces 90 percent of the nation's durum crop.[45]

As early as 1891 Ladd was experimenting with growing sugarbeets in North Dakota, although he was not one of the early "boomers" for this crop. In 1891 he wrote: "For the present it is my belief that for most of North Dakota other industries will be found more profitable for both manufacturer and farmer than the sugarbeet industry." By 1897-1898 he was more optimistic, but he still found most of the beets grown in North Dakota in 1898 to be low in sugar content.[46]

In some cases Ladd's researches and activities overlapped those of his colleagues. Such was the case in treating wheat seed with stronger solutions of formaldehyde to prevent stinking smut. Henry Luke Bolley had pioneered this treatment, but some farmers complained that the formaldehyde solutions on the market were not effective. Ladd analyazed 19 samples of commercial formaldehyde and found that 14 were below the standard of 40 percent strength of pure formaldehyde. In 1905 the Legislature passed a law to prevent the adulteration of formaldehyde sold in North Dakota and another law to provide an appropriation of $6,000 to the Experiment Station to enforce the former law.[47]

In 1905 North Dakota enacted a new state drug law and amended the food act to require a statement of quantity of contents. After checking with the Federal Bureau of Chemistry, Ladd decided not to prosecute for the quantity of contents if it was as often above as below the stated amount on the label. The 1905 law also required that the identity of the manufacturer or person responsible for the product must be on the label.[48]

While there may be some controversy as to whether Ladd had much influence on the pure food crusade on the federal level, he was active on the national scene in the Association of Agricultural Chemists, which helped to develop and improve chemical analyses. His stature and influence is attested to by his election as president of that body for one year.[49] Ladd was also active in the Association of State and National Food and Dairy Departments and he was president of that body in 1907.[50]

Ladd believed that the only way food and drug laws could be effective was to have uniform laws in all the states. By 1908 he was advocating a model state law, and of course, he backed the federal law. The way the federal law was enforced led Ladd into conflict with long-time Secretary of Agriculture James Wilson. Ladd believed that generally Secretary Wilson had served farmers well, but he scored him when he at times overruled Dr. Harvey W. Wiley on food and drug matters.[51]

Ladd believed that publicity had made the North Dakota law effective. In 1912 he stated: "Publicity has been the strong point emphasized since the enactment of the food and drug laws of the state and publicity has done more to correct evils of food adulteration than all other factors combined in this state."[52]

Whether or not Ladd's publicity was effective in enforcing pure food and drug laws, his activities in that field certainly made him a figure of consequence in North Dakota. Much, or maybe all, of his later career as a college administrator and politician stems from the image he built up as a pure food crusader. Dr. Wiley did not exaggerate in 1925 when he stated upon Ladd's death: "...I think undoubtedly he was the most popular man in North Dakota. The people of his state believed in him; they knew he was absolutely honest and incorruptible...."[53]

Ladd's image with the North Dakota public did not mean that everyone viewed him favorably. The conservative ex-congressman, Burleigh F. Spalding of North Dakota, wrote about Ladd in his autobiography: "...he had been one of the most distinguished examples of the effect of self-advertising that the country had seen. He had brought his notoriety about by securing the enactment of pure food and other similar laws in the state and in attempting to enforce them.... For years one could scarcely pick up a state paper without reading some laudatory article regarding Ladd or his work as Pure Food Commissioner and in his other offices...."[54]

The Spalding interpretation has not been generally accepted and the suspicion that Ladd, and other Progressive leaders, were merely empire building has generally received short shrift from historians. Eminent North Dakota historian Elwyn B. Robinson does go so far, however, as to refer to Ladd's publicity, or desire for it, as "his flair (almost mania) for publicity."[55] By 1915 Ladd had arrived at such a stage of his career that his alma mater, the University of Maine, awarded him an honorary doctorate and he was often called on to speak outside of North Dakota. In 1915 he addressed the International Congress of Medicine at Stanford University. He spoke on "Pure Paint" at the University of Minnesota in the same year, and he talked on the "Present Status of Food Legislation" at the Congress of Agriculture in San Francisco.[56] Soon thereafter, when President John H. Worst was relieved of his duties by the Board of the Agricultural College, the members asked Ladd if he would serve as acting president of the College until they found a suitable candidate. According to one recollection of the event, Ladd replied that he would serve as head of the College if the Board would remove the "acting" from the title. He assured the Board that he would resign from the position as soon as it found a capable replacement. When the secretary was about to enter this agreement into writing, Board member J.B. Power said this would be a reflection on Ladd and that his "word could be safely taken." In his autobiography, Spalding continued the account: "Humanity is fallible and sometimes forgetful. When the Board was ready to act and called on the Professor, it is said that he had experienced a lapse of memory and had no recollection of having been elected a temporary president, or that there had been any understanding that he would resign whenever the Board desired to replace him by a permanent President.[61]

Spalding believed that the reason the Board did not relieve Ladd at that point was because his publicity had been so effective, especially among North Dakota women, that it did not dare replace him. So Ladd remained president of the College until he went to the U.S. Senate in 1921.[58]

In spite of his many fine characteristics Ladd was in some ways unsuited for his position as president of the Agricultural College. His presidency was described by W.C. Hunter: "As head of the College he was dogmatic, frequently arbitrary, yet sincerely desirous of furthering the welfare of the faculty and that of the College."[59] One authority goes much deeper into probing the reasons for Ladd's disappointing career as president. He argues that Ladd was born in a period when such figures as Darwin were rejecting the comfortable old doctrine of absolutes, of right and wrong, and Ladd simply held on to an older view of things in a changing world. The argument goes further: "To Ladd right was right and wrong was wrong...his morality was couched in terms of black and white...this simple approach to life both promoted and restricted the effectiveness of his work."[60] This type of outlook was not suitable in a position that required compromises, in a situation where tact and flexibility were called for, and where the values were not "black and white."[61] In reviewing the events of Ladd's presidency, one has the impression of a well-meaning man caught in the web of his own character. The Ladd presidency, from 1916 to 1921, was a transition period in the history of the College. Hunter argues that the older faculty members were no longer as concerned or enthusiastic as they were in the beginning. The Ladds, Henry Luke Bolleys, and others were being shunted aside by younger men and women. Often the younger group had better professional credentials than the older. This may help explain the "Incident of 1916," when Bolley, the botanist, was accused of unprofessional methodology by younger professors. Members of the Board of Trustees apparently were soon unhappy with their selection of Ladd as president. They intensified their attacks on Bolley and added Alfred G. Arvold of the Little Country Theatre and C.B. Waldron to their list of undesirables holding positions at the Agricultural College.[62]

Both Hunter and Professor O.A. Stevens, long-time botanist of the Fargo institution, believed that one of Ladd's greatest weaknesses as an administrator was his excessive attention to detail. A friend of Stevens told him: "Your President is a detail man. Such seldom make good administrators."[63] A sampling of Ladd's correspondence as president seems to substantiate that view. In the period between 1916 and 1920 he wrote his assistants or the general faculty about commencement exercises, wartime growing of vegetables, college property, political activity by college employees, salaries and expenses, departmental budgets, and other miscellaneous matters.[64] While any president might want to deal with such subjects, most administrators would delegate many of these matters to assistants. Ladd's major problem, though, was that he had no assistants in those days before decentralization.

Ladd did some work in creating an administrative structure more appropriate to a maturing College. In 1916 the Board accepted President Ladd's reorganization plan, a proposal calling for the creation of the schools of Agriculture, Home Economics, Education, Chemistry and Pharmacy, Veterinary Science, Arts and Sciences, and Engineering and Mechanic Arts.[65] The small institution that began in temporary quarters in another college with only four instructors in 1890 had indeed grown and matured by 1916. Ladd's plan was a sound one and he deserves full credit for it.

A glimpse of the Ladds as a presidential family was provided by Miss Pearl Dinan, formerly English instructor and dean of women at the Agricultural College. Miss Dinan, as a friend of the Ladd family, had opportunities to view the rather formal hospitality President Ladd extended to faculty and staff and the more warm graciousness of Southern-born Rizpah Ladd. Mrs. Ladd's charm often softened Ladd's more brusque behavior. The Ladds entertained the faculty yearly at a formal dance in the field house. A week later they were in the habit of receiving students and new faculty. In addition they continued their memorable open-handed hospitality toward their friends.[66]

Perhaps Ladd's greatest achievement as College president, along with his reorganization plan, was his continuation of the Worst tradition of a strong faculty teaching students a core of practical courses combined with a curriculum of liberal arts. Even then there were those who wanted to make the institution a political football and to confine its offerings to a narrowly practical program.[67]

Ladd's career as College president ended with his entry into national politics when he ran as the Nonpartisan candidate for the U.S. Senate in 1920. In the Republican primary of June 30, 1920, he defeated A.J. Gronna for the Republican nomination by a vote of 54,947 to 51,152. In the general election in the fall that year, he overcame his Democratic opponent by a margin in excess of 40,000.[68]

Ladd's major concern in the Senate was the farm problem. He was a Farm Bloc senator[69] who believed that farmers needed better credit and marketing conditions, larger appropriations for research on their behalf, and better interstate cooperation.[70] Ladd also wanted a cheap source of fertilizer—which recalled his research days at the New York Experiment Station at Geneva—and for that reason, among others, he supported the Henry Ford Muscle Shoals project in the Tennessee Valley. The Muscle Shoals project would convert the Wilson Dam, which had been built by the government during World War I, to use for overall flood control, to generate electricity, and to produce nitrogen for fertilizer either under private or government control. Ladd opted for private control while his Progressive colleague, Senator George Norris of Nebraska, came out for government control. Ultimately, Congress created the Tennessee Valley Authority as a federal project in the 1930s.[71]

As a Farm Bloc senator, Ladd recommended legislation to control filled milk, which is substituting other fats for milkfat producing an artificial product. He spoke for a high tariff and he sponsored legislation to fight speculation in farm products and to establish cooperative marketing associations.[72] One of the reasons he wanted to recognize Bolshevik Russia was to find more farm markets.[73]

Ladd took a firm stand in the Senate by being consistently against profiteering by banks and he supported truth-in-labeling legislation. He had a part in the Teapot Dome investigations, although not a major one.[74] He also brought about investigations of various enterprises at home and overseas.[75]

Ladd's foreign policy views were about half isolationist and half pacifist. He sincerely wanted to prevent war, he wanted legislation to prevent American businesses from interfering in the affairs of other nations, and he believed a referendum should be held on declarations of war.[76] Ladd also advocated that the United States recognize the governments of both Mexico and Russia because he wanted to open up markets for farmers in the two countries.[77] Particularly regarding Russia, Ladd seems to have been handicapped by a good deal of naivete. Although he visited Communist Russia,[78] he still came away believing Russia was not controlled by the teachings of the Communist Party! Such views in foreign policy were shared by other Progressives such as Robert LaFollette of Wisconsin and would not be considered radical today now that recognition has come about.[79]

Ladd considered himself a member of the "radical" or LaFollette group in the Senate.[80] He joined the LaFollette revolt from the Republican Party in 1924 and as a result was disciplined by Republican leaders in the Senate. He maintained, though, that he was still a Republican and that only the people of North Dakota could judge the right or wrong of his stand when they voted in the presidential election in 1924.[81] Republican senators agreed that Ladd was the right person to represent the people of North Dakota, the best example being conservative Senator Bert M. Fernald from Ladd's home state of Maine.[82]

Generally speaking, the Farm Bloc failed in most of its legislative objectives although it was upholding Progressive goals of 1900-1917 and responding to the collapse of farm prices in the 1920s. Minor advances in the agricultural program did not alleviate the depressed condition of farming in the 1920s. Ladd did not secure cheap fertilizer for farmers, nor did he improve the farmers' position in the world market. Ladd's truth-in-labeling legislation was at least favorably received, but there was no end to "profiteering" in the grain markets (or elsewhere). In foreign policy Ladd was a full decade ahead of his time. Recognition of Soviet Russia did not come until 1933 and nothing really concrete was done by the U.S. Senate to prevent future wars—in spite of naval disarmament and other moves in that direction. One of his biographers, in a somewhat negative vein, summed up Ladd's senatorial career by asserting: "In short, one can search in vain for momentous accomplishments in the Senate career of Edwin Fremont Ladd."[83]

In spite of being a junior senator, Ladd became well-known and possibly influential in his short tenure in the Senate. He was a valuable adviser for other senators because of his scientific and agricultural background. His revolt in 1924 displayed his political independence and probably made him better-known than most other freshman senators. He was involved in conducting the Teapot Dome investigations and considered himself a LaFollette-Norris "radical" bloc member. His loyalty to the Nonpartisan League, though, was marginal; he did little campaigning for League candidates and did not concern himself with League affairs. He might have faced a tough fight for re-election in a state that had reverted to conservatism had he lived.[84]

Probably the most perplexing stand taken by Ladd in the Congress was his support for Henry Ford's plan for private development of Muscle Shoals, the heart of which became the Tennessee Valley Authority. From his written statements and from his membership in the LaFollette-Norris bloc one would assume that Ladd would have supported government development of Muscle Shoals.[85] His reasons for supporting the Ford proposal seem to have boiled down to a belief that development of the Muscle Shoals project would lead the government into the "uncharted field of power and fertilizer production." Ladd issued a minority report, signed by Arthur Capper of Kansas and five Cotton Bloc members of the Senate Agricultural Committee in 1922, that called for the unconditional acceptance of the Ford offer. He believed this was the path to cheap fertilizer for American farmers and that the project would serve as "an example for the development of cheap water power all over America." Perhaps Ladd was also blinded by the Ford image in the 1920s. The great industrialist had brought Americans the cheap car they wanted and he paid his workers $5 a day. Why wouldn't he be the person to develop Muscle Shoals? There was even a "Ford for President" boomlet in the 1920s.[86] These seem rather weak reasons, however, for abandoning the more Progressive position of favoring government ownership of utilities.

When Ladd died of kidney failure in 1925, he had served as a teacher, chemist, researcher, pure food crusader, college president and U.S. senator. His academic career divides mainly into three distinct activities—as chemist, teacher, and academic administator. For his day and time, Ladd seems to have been a qualified chemist. Both at the New York Station and in Fargo he embarked on investigations that were needed by the agricultural public. He wrote very little. His *Manual of Quantitative Chemical Analysis* was his sole venture into the world of academic publication other than Experiment Station bulletins. That Ladd, without any graduate training, could have performed so well as a chemist speaks well for his undergraduate training, the quality of his experiences in New York, and his intelligence and ability to learn on his own.

As a teacher, Ladd had more problems than he did as a chemist. Seeing only the right and wrong in situations, he sometimes did not see clearly his own participation in events. He was incensed by cheating on campus. And yet, his two daughters—who were students at the time—maintained that the cheating was worse in Ladd's own classes! The daughters maintained they did not tell him the true situation because it would have hurt his feelings. More likely, they were inhibited by his rather stern behavior.[87] Ladd's performance as college president was disappointing, according to Hunter. The Agricultural College historian notes that Ladd was swamped in detail and that he was dogmatic. Yet, he wisely reorganized a college that had grown like Topsy, bringing about order where there had been chaos. He ensured the survival of a strong faculty at the Agricultural College and with it a strong offering. His handling of the accusations against H.L. Bolley in the "Incident of 1916" was good and the investigation of the problem was conducted along ethical lines. The portrait of Ladd as president is one of a vigorous executive who handled problems well.

But Ladd's reputation was mainly based on his role in the pure food crusade in North Dakota. If the national pure food crusade was led by Harvey W. Wiley, then the North Dakota pure food crusade was Ladd's story. From its inception Ladd nurtured the program, used his publicity to bolster it, and only when he was called to wider fields of activity in the academic world and the Senate did he move away from the program. His pure food program ultimately attracted the support of both conservatives and progressives. Progressives believed the program would help consumers and conservatives often supported progressive-led regulation because they thought they could control and profit from the laws. The notoriety Ladd gained through his espousal of the pure food crusade thrust him into the presidential chair at the Agricultural College and, later, into a seat in the U.S. Senate.

Ladd's role as U.S. senator was essentially that of a junior senator. From that position he diligently worked to benefit the farmers of North Dakota and, more broadly, farmers in the United States. He belonged to the LaFollette-Norris Progressive wing, yet he took a position opposite to his faction on public ownership of utilities when he backed Henry Ford's plan for private ownership of Muscle Shoals. He may have been impressed with Ford's image in the 1920s but the best guess as to why he supported private ownership is that he thought Ford could deliver power and fertilizer cheaper and quicker than government. In foreign policy Senator Ladd was a decade ahead of most Americans in his demand for the recognition of Soviet Russia. He also wanted to establish relations with Mexico and he favored a referendum before war with any hostile country could be declared. Most of Ladd's senatorial proposals failed. He accomplished nothing of a "momentous" nature, but much of what he advocated in domestic and foreign affairs later came to pass and has been accepted by Americans today.

Ladd's career in the service of North Dakota was a relatively long one. He accomplished a good deal on the college and state level. He was an astute manager of public opinion and carried the North Dakota public with him in the pure food crusade, in his role as college president and as U.S. senator. In the Senate as a member of the Farm Bloc and the LaFollette Progressive group, he and those groups advocated progressive goals and ideals that would eventually be incorporated in government policy and that would affect the way Americans live today.

Edwin Ladd directed chemistry teaching and research from a large
building at the center of campus. It burned in 1907 and was rebuilt
in 1910. The chemistry building was renamed in honor of Ladd in
1952.

A paint factory on the NDAC campus made colored paints, varnishes and linseed oil from flax. The paints were tested on Ladd's paint fences stationed about the campus.

In 1916 Edwin Ladd succeeded John Henry Worst as president of NDAC. Four years later Ladd posed with his family while he successfully campaigned for the U.S. Senate.

Edwin Fremont Ladd

Footnotes

[1]Ralph J. Kane, *Edwin Fremont Ladd: North Dakota's Pure-Food Crusader,* Master of Arts thesis, the University of North Dakota, August 1960, pp. 34-35. See also Dumas Malone, editor, *Dictionary of American Biography,* Vol. V (New York, 1933).

[2]Vernon Ladd to Dr. Franz H. Rathmann, March 31, 1964. The letter is located in the Edwin F. Ladd Papers, North Dakota State University, Fargo, North Dakota. Rathmann, a professor at North Dakota State University, wrote *Seventy Five Years of Chemistry and Related Science at North Dakota State University* (Fargo: North Dakota State University, 1965.) Upon the seventy-fifth anniversary of the University the chemistry building was renamed Ladd Hall.

[3]E. Vernon Ladd to Kane, July 20, 1959, as quoted in Kane, *Pure-Food Crusader,* p. 35.

[4]Robinson, *History of North Dakota,* pp. 261-262.

[5]"Senator Ladd Passes On," *Brotherhood of Locomotive Firemen and Engineer's Magazine* (July, 1925) Vol. 79, No. 1, p. 45, and Kane, *Pure-Food Crusader,* p. 35. The magazine article is located in Ladd Papers, NDIRS.

[6]Kane, *Pure-Food Crusade,* pp. 35-36, information stemming from George H. Crosby, Jr., registrar of the University of Maine, to Kane, July 14, 1959.

[7]*Ibid.,* p. 36.

[8]*Ibid.* Information from E. Vernon Ladd to Kane, July 20, 1959.

[9]Letter from John F. Collins Jr., registrar, University of Maine at Orono, to Bill G. Reid, December 7, 1981.

[10]A good survey for this period of Ladd's life is found in Kane, *Pure-Food Crusade,* pp. 36-37.

[11]"Ladd and After," *Boston Daily Globe,* June 23, 1925, clipping in Ladd Papers, NDIRS.

[12]Kane, *Pure-Food Crusade,* pp. 36-37. See Margaret Rossiter for ag chemists and fertilizers.

[13]H.L. Bolley, "E.F. Ladd," *Chemical Bulletin,* September 1925, clipping in Ladd Papers, NDIRS, no pagination given.

[14]Culver Ladd to Kane, August 2, 1959, as quoted in Kane, *Pure-Food Crusade,* p. 39.

[15]Bolley, "E.F. Ladd," *Chemical Bulletin,* no page given, Ladd Papers, NDIRS. See also Kane, *Pure-Food Crusade,* pp. 40-41, for Ladd's personal appearance.

[16]Rathmann, *Seventy Five Years of Chemistry,* p. 3. See also Hunter, *Beacon Across the Prairie,* pp. 22-25. See also Kane, *Pure-Food Crusade,* pp. 221-222.

[17]*Ibid.*

[18]*Ibid.*

[19]*Ibid.,* p. 4. See also Kane, *Pure-Food Crusade,* p. 221.

[20]*Ibid.,* pp. 3-4. See Walster, "Edwin F. Ladd," in *Five for the Land,* pp. 26-34, for Ladd and paint.

[21]See E.F. Ladd to J.C. Wade, Jamestown, North Dakota, January 27, 1891, Ladd Papers, NDIRS, for a sample letter along these lines. See also Josiah Shull, president, New York Dairymen's Association, to E.F. Ladd, November 16, 1891, in E.F. Ladd Papers, North Dakota State Historical Society, Bismarck, North Dakota. Hereinafter referred to as Ladd Papers, NDSHS. The Bismarck Papers add very little to what is known about Ladd.

[22]See E.F. Ladd to S.H. Cork, Fargo, North Dakota, October 18, 1891, Ladd Papers, NDIRS, for an example of these activities. See also Francis A. Hart, clerk of district court, Pembina County, to E.F. Ladd, February 6, 1897, NDSHS for these activities.

[23]Walster, "Edwin F. Ladd" in *Five for the Land,* pp. 60-64.

[24]E.F. Ladd to J.K. West, Detroit (Lakes), Minnesota, May 7, 1891, Ladd Papers, NDIRS.

[25]Vernon Ladd to Franz H. Rathmann, March 31, 1964. Ladd Papers, NDIRS. For the long quote on Rizpah, Ladd consulted Kane, *Pure-Food Crusade,* pp. 49-50. For names of children, consult Alfred C. Melby, *A Chemist in the Senate: Edwin Fremont Ladd, 1921-1925* (Grand Forks: UND Thesis, 1967), p. 5 (also for tennis, gardening and hunting bison).

[26]William C. Hunter, *Beacon Across the Prairie: North Dakota's Land-Grant College* (Fargo: NDIRS, 1961), p. 100.

[27]H.L. Walster, "Edwin Fremont Ladd - Chemist," un-published manuscript, Ladd Papers, NDIRS, p. 5.

[28]Vernon Ladd to Franz H. Rathmann, March 31, 1964, Ladd Papers, NDIRS.

[29]Kane, *Pure-Food Crusade,* p. 48.

[30]Rathmann, *Seventy Five Years of Chemistry,* pp. 3-4.

[31]Oscar E. Anderson, Jr., *The Health of a Nation: Harvey W. Wiley and the Fight for Pure Food* (Chicago: the University of Chicago Press, 1958), p. 197.

[32]W.C. Palmer, "Professor E.F. Ladd," p. 53, typescript in the Ladd Papers, NDIRS. Palmer was an editor on the Agricultural College Campus from 1910-1947. See also Fred B. Linton, "State Food Law Leaders—Ladd of North Dakota Pioneers in Food Law Enforcement," *Food, Drugs, Cosmetic Law Journal* VII (May 1952), p. 314. See also Walster, "Edwin F. Ladd," p. 11, for local conditions.

[33]Kane, *Pure-Food Crusade,* p. 144. "The Alsop process used an electric flame to generate intense heat which caused oxygen and nitrogen to fuse forming nitrogen peroxide. It was the presence of this residue of nitrogen peroxide in bleached flour that prompted Ladd to rule that the Alsop process violated the pure-food law. Judge Charles (A.) Pollock issued an injunction in favor of the plaintiffs (four local millers), but Ladd questioned the court's jurisdiction in limiting the actions of a public official. On appeal the North Dakota Supreme Court ruled that the plaintiffs did have the right to seek relief in the state courts."

[34]Erling Nicolari Rolfsrud, *Lanterns Over the Prairie,* Book II (Brainerd, Minnesota: Lakeland Press, 1950), p. 119. See also Walster, "Edwin Fremont

Ladd," Ladd Papers, NDIRS, p. 4 and p. 17. For the judges and Ladd, the Alsop process, and out-of-state pure food crusades see Kane, *Pure-Food Crusade*, p. 219. See *Ibid.*, p. 218, for lack of food manufacturing in North Dakota.

[35]Walster, "Edwin Fremont Ladd," p. 4.

[36]*Ibid.*

[37]Linton, "State Food Law Leaders," p. 314.

[38]*Ibid.*

[39]*Ibid.*, p. 316

[40]Zena Irma Trinka, *North Dakota Today*, 3rd edition, (St. Paul: Louis F. Dow Co., 1920), p. 167.

[41]Linton, "State Food Law Leaders," p. 316.

[42]*Ibid.*, p. 318

[43]"The A.C. Mill," typescript, no author or date information given, Ladd Papers, NDIRS. K.A. Gilles and L.D. Sibbitt, "Sixty Years of Cereal Technology at North Dakota State University," North Dakota Agricultural Experiment Station, Fargo, North Dakota, Journal Series No. 58, p. 2874. Walster, "Edwin F. Ladd," pp. 53-54.

[44]Walster, "Edwin F. Ladd," pp. 42-43.

[45]*Ibid.*, pp. 55-58.

[46]*Ibid.*, pp. 23-26

[47]*Ibid.*, pp. 35-37.

[48]Linton, "State Food Law Leaders," p. 319.

[49]*Ibid.*

[50]*Ibid.*, p. 320

[51]*Ibid.*, pp. 320-321.

[52]*Ibid.*, p. 319.

[53]Copy (handwritten) of Harvey W. Wiley's comments upon Ladd's death, Ladd Papers, NDIRS.

[54]Burleigh F. Spalding Papers, NDIRS, "Autobiography," p. 42.

[55]Robinson, *History of North Dakota*, p. 261.

[56]Rolfsrud, *Lanterns Over the Prairie*, p. 119. See also Kane, *Pure-Food Crusade*, p. 211.

[57]Spalding, "Autobiography," Spalding Papers, NDIRS., p. 42.

[58]*Ibid.*

[59]Hunter, *Beacon Across the Prairie*, p. 100.

[60]Kane, *Pure-Food Crusade*, p. 214.

[61]*Ibid.*

[62]Interview by the writer with Professor Emeritus O.A. Stevens of the Botany Department of North Dakota State University, June 14, 1968. Herbert E. Gason, "Ladd Asked to Quit," from Fargo *Courier-News*, July 2, 1917, in *The Nonpartisan Leader*, July 5, 1917.

[63]Hunter, *Beacon Across the Prairie*, pp. 99-100, and Stevens Interview, June 14, 1968.

[64]Ladd Outgoing Letters, 1916-1920, Ladd Papers, NDIRS.

[65]Clare B. Waldron, a mimeographed history of the North Dakota

Agricultural College, 1931, p. 21 , in the Clare B. Waldron Papers, NDIRS.

[66]Interview by the writer with Miss Pearl Dinan, June 28, 1968.

[67]Rathmann, *Seventy Five Years of Chemistry, p. 4.*

[68]*Lewis F. Crawford, History of North Dakota*, Vol. I (Chicago and New York: The American Historical Society, Inc., 1931), pp. 439-440.

[69]Alfred C. Melby, *A Chemist in the Senate*, University of North Dakota master's thesis, 1967, p. 111.

[70]*Ibid.* See also E.F. Ladd, "Endowment of Agricultural Stations," speech in the Senate, February 19, 1925, wherein Ladd specifically called for more appropriations for research.

[71]Melby, *Chemist in the Senate*, p. 112. See also Edwin F. Ladd, "Why I Am For Henry Ford's Offer For Muscle Shoals," *The Saturday Evening Post*, November 29, 1929, and Edwin F. Ladd, "St. Lawrence Seaway vs. Oswego-Hudson Ship Canal," speech in the Senate, February 28, 1925. For Norris' views see George W. Norris, *Fighting Liberal, Autobiography* (New York: The Macmillan Co., (1946), pp. 245-259.

[72]Melby, *Chemist in the Senate*, p. 112.

[73]*Ibid.*

[74]*Ibid.*, and see also the *Wenatchee Daily World* (Washington State) May 25, 1925, clipping in the Ladd Papers, NDIRS.

[75]Melby, *Chemist in the Senate*, p. 112.

[76]*Ibid.*, pp. 112-113.

[77]E.F. Ladd, "Our Duty to Mexico, Recognition of Mexican Government, Why is Mexico Not Recognized by the United States?" speech in the Senate, July 19, 1922, clipping located in E.F. Ladd Papers, NDIRS , and Edwin Fremont Ladd, "Our Failure to Recognize Russia Keeps Door Closed to Vast Domain of Natural Wealth" A Striking Statement by Edwin Fremont Ladd, U.S. Senator from North Dakota, *The Magazine of Wall Street*, March 29, 1924, clipping in Ladd Papers, NDIRS.

[78]"Ladd and King Take Own Food to Russia," undated, no newspaper title clipping in Ladd Paper, NDIRS.

[79]"Senator Ladd on Trade Relations," undated, no newspaper title, clipping in Ladd Papers, NDIRS. See Belle Case and Fole LaFollette, *Robert M. LaFollette* (New York: MacMillan Co., 1953), Vol. 2, p. 938.

[80]U.S. Senator Edwin Fremont Ladd, "What Do We Radicals Want? A Plain Statement of the Purposes of the Progressive Wing," *The Magazine of Wall Street*, December 9, 1922, clipping in Ladd Paper, NDIRS.

[81]Edwin F. Ladd, "My Constituents the Judges," speech in the Senate, January 6, 1925.

[82]"Senator Ladd Not a Party Wrecker," Portland (Maine) *Evening Express*, March 12, 1925, clipping in Ladd Papers, NDIRS.

[83]Melby, *Chemist in the Senate*, p. 113.

[84]Melby, *Chemist in the Senate*, pp. 113-114. For the situation in North Dakota concerning the upcoming election of 1926 consult "As Seen Through Smoked Glass," *The McLean County* (North Dakota) *Independent*, June 4, 1925; "How Senator Ladd Stands With League," *McLean County* (North

Dakota) *Independent,* June 18, 1924; and "That Opposition to Ladd," North Dakota *Nonpartisan,* no date, all clippings in Ladd Papers, NDIRS.

[85]U.S. Senator Edwin Fremont Ladd, "What Do We Radicals Want? A Plain Statement of the Purposes of the Progressive Wing," *The Magazine of Wall Street,* December 9, 1922, clipping in Ladd Papers, NDIRS for Ladd's support of government ownership of utilities.

[86]"Muscle Shoals Views," 67th Congress, Second Session, Report 831, Part 2, pp. 1-19. See also Preston J. Hubbard, *Origins of the TVA: The Muscle Shoals Controversy, 1920-1932* (Nashville: Vanderbilt University Press, 1961), pp. 77-78.

[87]Interview by the writer with Miss Pearl Dinan, June 28, 1968, for the cheating story. The interpretation presented here of the event is my own.

John Shepperd

John Henry Shepperd, Animal Scientist as Story Writer and College Administrator

John Henry Shepperd joined the group of trained scientists at North Dakota Agricultural College and Experiment Station in 1893, swelling the total staff number to ten. It was a young College and Station served by a young and ambitious staff, and Shepperd added his youthful enthusiasm when he replaced his brother-in-law, W.M. Hays, who went to the University of Minnesota.[1]

John Henry Shepperd was born in January 1869 in Chariton, Lucas County, Iowa.[2] The Shepperds were a pioneering clan. Shepperd's grandfather emigrated from Scotland to North Carolina and then to southern Indiana where the community still had to maintain a block house as a shelter against Indian attack. In 1851 Shepperd's father moved from Indiana to southern Iowa where John, the youngest of seven children, was born.[3] Shepperd's youthful experiences were typical for a farm youth in the Corn Belt in the 19th century. He went to the district school in the winter and the rest of the time helped out with plowing and cutting and husking corn. Even in those early years he showed a definite predilection for livestock work, busying himself with his father's herd of Shorthorn cattle.[4] He also received early training in agribusiness there on the farm when an older brother paid him a nickel a day to husk corn. When he used his meager earnings to buy a pig, he later said: "It was not a business proposition, for I bought this little animal for purely aesthetic reasons—the desire to have a pet."[5] This episode indicated the love of animal life that would propel him into a crusade for an improved livestock industry in North Dakota.[6]

He completed the first eight grades in district school, then went on to Drake University in Des Moines, Iowa, in the fall of 1883. An older brother, Bruce, was teaching there and Shepperd enrolled in the preparatory department, taking accounting. Later he enrolled in the academic courses, but Shepperd soon determined that Greek, Latin and mathematics were not sufficiently practical to suit his tastes.[7]

At home for the Christmas holidays, Shepperd read a report by W.H. Brewer, professor of agriculture at the University of

Minnesota, that caused him to go to Iowa State Agricultural College at Ames for an education in agriculture. At the Iowa college he was the only student in agriculture for his freshman, sophomore and junior years and when he graduated with honors in 1891, he was the only agricultural graduate that year. Another famous graduate of Iowa State Agricultural College, George Washington Carver, entered the year Shepperd graduated.[8]

In addition to agricultural courses, he took spoken and written English, mathematics and related subjects, physical sciences, biological sciences, German, history, and military science. Although his specialty was agriculture, he nevertheless obtained a general education.[9]

In the year following his graduation Shepperd spent six months in agricultural study at the University of Minnesota, then spent a year at the University of Wisconsin studying livestock. Wisconsin awarded him a master of science degree in 1893.[10]

Shepperd picked up some of his germinal ideas concerning agriculture and livestock from his college instructors. At Iowa State he was influenced by James Wilson, who later became U.S. Secretary of Agriculture, and Charles F. Curtiss, who later became dean of agriculture and director of the Experiment Station at Iowa. At Wisconsin, Shepperd came under the influence of John A. Craig, a brilliant and pioneering animal husbandman. Craig helped originate livestock judging as a means of teaching animal science, and much of Shepperd's life-long interest in judging stems from his study under Craig.[11]

Shepperd's first position after graduate school involved writing a series of articles for the Chicago-based farm weekly, the *Orange Judd Farmer*. As assistant editor for the journal, he sharpened his writing skills, which were already considerable.[12]

Shepperd accepted a position as professor of agriculture with the newly organized North Dakota Agricultural College and Experiment Station and began his work on November 1, 1893. At the time there were only two buildings on campus, the administration building (College Hall, later to be called Old Main) and Francis Hall where Shepperd boarded. College Hall provided space for offices, classrooms, and laboratories, and the tower room was the president's office. The library was also housed there. The unfinished third floor was the gymnasium used by both faculty and students. The campus itself was set in the middle of a wheat field a mile or more from the nearest Fargo residential section.[13]

Shepperd recalled the time he began his work at the

Agricultural College: "When I began work at the AC on November 1, 1893, I met a staff of nine other men.... My arrival swelled the force of scientific workers to ten men and we carried the beginnings of college teaching, Experiment Station research, and agricultural extension work. Of course, all of these functions were meager...."[14] In addition to his work as professor of agriculture and agriculturalist in the Experiment Station, Shepperd taught arithmetic in the preparatory department. During the period James Buel Power served as acting president following the removal of Horace E. Stockbridge, Shepperd was appointed acting director of the Experiment Station.[15]

In those early days, Professor Shepperd remembered, the institution had about 30 to 40 students, the experimental work was good, but limited, and the extension work consisted of some farmers' institutes and writing for the *Dakota Farmer* and for the daily and weekly press. Needless to say, the early-day staff members earned their pay by their versatility as well as by their long hours.[16]

It was the custom in those days to have a faculty meeting once a week and an Experiment Station staff meeting once a month. Shepperd recalled: "I remember well the faculty meetings which were held in the President's Office every Friday afternoon. I can to this day point out where each member sat. Once a month the Experiment Station members met. Those of us who were both teachers and investigators remained for our session after the teachers had retired. The President was also Director of the Experiment Station so that there was no change in chairman for the second meeting...."[17]

During those first years students studied largely agriculture, domestic economy, chemistry, veterinary science, horticulture, biology, mechanics, mathematics, English, geography, and history. Degree courses in agriculture, engineering, and applied science were offered as required by the Morrill Act. Other courses were developed later.[18]

When Shepperd arrived in Fargo, he was a young bachelor and boarded at Francis Hall. On July 3, 1895, he married Adele Taylor, affectionately known as "Dell," and brought his bride back to Fargo. She had been raised on a neighboring farm in Iowa and had attended Drake University. She attended North Dakota Agricultural College, specializing in chemistry, and she became Edwin F. Ladd's assistant for a long period. The childless couple were mutually supportive and participated actively in social affairs for the students and faculty. Mrs. Shepperd was also an active club woman for a quarter of a century.[19]

A good teacher, Shepperd took an abiding interest in his students. He corresponded with them, encouraged them to remain in or return to school and he took them on stock judging tours. Of course, he was able to do this because he had relatively few students at a given time. Still, he went out of his way to help, often seeking employment for his charges.[20]

As agriculturalist of the College and Station, Shepperd was constantly looking for improved strains of crops or livestock that would benefit North Dakota farmers. Some agricultural historians argue that most U.S. Department of Agriculture programs were not designed to benefit farmers, but to make agriculture conform to the needs of urban society. This was not Shepperd's goal or idea.

One problem with North Dakota agriculture in the early 20th century was the fact that hard spring wheat did not do well in the western and drier regions of the state. Shepperd thought he had found the solution when Mark A. Carleton, USDA cerealist, discovered that durum, or macaroni wheat (particularly Kubanka) did so well in those areas. Carleton collected samples of durum in Russia in 1898-1900. Shepperd became an enthusiastic champion of durum wheat, and was appointed to a committee of three by the Tri-State Grain Growers Convention to advance the interests of durum wheat and its producers. He received numerous letters from people interested in macaroni wheat and was impatient with millers who discriminated against the new variety.[21]

But Shepperd's great love was livestock, especially dairy animals. One of this first actions when joining the Fargo agricultural staff was to buy a herd of dairy cows and to put dairying into the agricultural program. His work with dairy animals was also supported by Edwin F. Ladd. One of Shepperd's proudest accomplishments was the formation of the New Salem, North Dakota, Breeding Circuit. New Salem was a German settlement of both Reich Germans and Germans from Russia in the southwestern part of the state. The circuit, established in 1909 as the joint venture of the USDA, the North Dakota Experiment Station, and the New Salem Holstein Friesian Cattle Breeder's Association, furnished a means for testing for dairy herd improvement. The group established production records in 1910.[22]

In 1921 Shepperd published Extension Circular 45 "Wrong Side Up—The Indian's Dream, the White Man's Reality." It was the story of John Christiansen, an early settler of the New Salem region and an enterprising member of the New Salem Breeding Circuit. Central to the story was an old Indian telling Christiansen that plowing the virgin soil was turning the land "wrong side up." Shepperd agreed with the Indian's conservationist philosophy and he always advocated rotating crops, putting in pastures and storing feed in "fat years" to be used in the "lean years." Certainly the success of Christiansen and others like him supported Shepperd's argument for blooded stock, rotation, feed storage, and soil conservation. Shepperd, on behalf of the Experiment Station, was advocating mixed farming and cattle raising instead of one-crop farming of wheat in the West River country. This advice has been more than vindicated over time and today ranching is emphasized as much as farming. This reflects credit on Shepperd and points out the utility of the Experiment Station in an agricultural state.[23]

Shepperd was knowledgeable about livestock production, but how would he get those facts and figures to the public in an era before there was an extension service? Former journalist Shepperd naturally turned to the printed word and decided that the best way of spreading the word would be through the short story, devoid of technical language. This led to a series of articles, "The Northern Pig from Birth to Market," based on conversations with "Daddy" Geiken, the college herdsman. A later technique was to base his stories on conversations with a young grandnephew, John Budd Wentz. Thus, his career as a "story teller" was launched. The homey flavor of his Northern Pig stories is reflected in the following excerpt:

"Last spring I wanted to do some experiments with hogs and talked over my plans with Daddy Geiken, the college herdsman, telling him what I wanted to do.

" 'Then, I'll have to move Jennie,' Daddy said. Jennie was a Yorkshire sow with a nice litter of month-old pigs. 'Well, that is too bad—but if I've got to do that experiment I suppose I'll have to move her.'

" 'Why?' I asked. 'There is a place good enough for her with a good yard down in the north annex.' We call it a temporary addition on the north end of the college hog barn, the north annex.

" 'Oh! Jennie will fret a lot if I move her and there will be far less milk come for the pigs. How soon must you start that experiment?' My experiments always are making Daddy trouble.

" 'In a week or ten days,' I replied.

" 'Well, maybe I can get her to move and be satisfied by that time,' he said."[24]

But there was a deeper reason for Shepperd's resorting to the short story form in writing his bulletins. He believed he had inherited his father's penchant for telling stories. Still and all, he was an agriculturalist with the soul of a dreamer and story teller. Later he wrote: "Trained as a scientist, I was always exposed to those with the harsh viewpoint and was led to think those who resorted to figures of speech (and) stories and drama were nature fakers and worse than pseudo scientists...."[25] But his agricultural short stories were being well received as late as 1922.[26]

One very important aspect of Shepperd's life was his unending interest in livestock judging, particularly by students. It was in connection with the International Livestock Exposition that he did his most enduring work. There had been a similar contest at the Omaha Exposition of 1898, but the premier show was the International held annually in Chicago beginning in 1900. Shepperd became the superintendent in charge of International judging and filled that role from 1905 to 1938. It was one of his crowning achievements. In 1921 Shepperd was honored when he was asked to sit for his portrait with the noted Swedish portrait artist, Arvid Nyhold. The portrait was commissioned by the Saddle and Sirloin Club of Chicago and later hung there. Shepperd was justifiably pleased with the honor, writing his brother: "It (the portrait) will be the ninth college man's portrait to be hung in the gallery. They have to be formally voted in by the club and they are supposed to be very exclusive." He also noted that biographies of the portrait subjects were being prepared.[27]

At the University of Wisconsin Shepperd had developed an interest in dairying because of his opportunity to know Stephen M. Babcock, the inventor of the Babcock test for milk fat. Although North Dakota did not offer the same favorable environment for dairying as Wisconsin, Shepperd's interest in improving dairying continued and his last bulletin dealt with dairy cattle. He and his Station colleagues continued to work on North Dakota dairying, especially the problems of the harsh winters of the Northern Plains that killed out such traditional pasture crops as alfalfa. In 1900, Shepperd published an Experiment Station report stating that the alfalfa plants were not hardy enough to warrant sowing their seed. The Station staff, particularly L.R. Waldron, did not give up, but continued the search for a hardy variety. Ten years later, the Grimm strain of alfalfa was being grown by North Dakota farmers and ranchers.[28]

The federally funded Northern Great Plains Agricultural Experiment Station was established at Mandan in 1912-1913 primarily to furnish a spot to study livestock feeding. When the Mandan Station was founded, cooperative plans were made with the Animal Husbandry Department of the College. These involved establishing grazing trials to discover the carrying capacity of animals on a given tract of land with a certain forage growth. Shepperd's deep commitment to the Mandan Station stemmed from his belief that the Land Grant institution should serve all the regions of the state and his conviction that plowing under the native grass would be destructive to the soil. As a result of his involvement and competence, he was offered the post of superintendent of the Mandan Station.[29]

In addition to his work with livestock, Shepperd also made valuable contributions to the study of roots, plants, and improved varieties of grain. Grain growing was the industry of settled North Dakota when he arrived in 1893. His efforts gave the state new, superior varieties of wheat, oats, barley, and rye. Some of his varieties such as Dakold (ND 959) rye, for example, became standard for a long period. Shepperd was awarded a gold medal for his plant breeding work at the Paris World Exposition in 1900.[30]

Although Henry Luke Bolley achieved fame as the conquerer of flax wilt, it was Shepperd as acting director of the Experiment Station who called Bolley's attention to flax experiments at the University of Minnesota Experiment Station. In the flax experimentation Professor Edwin F. Ladd examined the soil and Bolley did the planting and selection. By 1908 Bolley was able to make the first distribution of strains of wilt-resistant flax.[31]

In spite of his significant achievements, Shepperd was not particularly well satisfied with Fargo and North Dakota. During the period 1904-1920 he applied for many positions throughout the country. Apparently he was dissatisfied with the frigid climate of the Northern Great Plains because most of the positions he sought were in the South. There were other problems, of course. There was friction at the College and possibly Shepperd saw the Board and administration as unsympathetic. Still, there were powerful forces that moved to keep Shepperd at the North Dakota institution, among these the forceful intervention of his friends and colleagues. In 1904, when Shepperd was considering a move to Tennessee, Edwin F. Ladd wrote him a letter that was friendly, forceful, and candid. "Pardon me if I am somewhat personal in what I say. I don't want to see you go.... You cannot afford to go without good reason. Your reputation is in North Dakota."[32] Ladd continued his argument: "North Dakota is a growing state, the institution new to develop with the state. Tenn. is old, fixed, Southern and every man in the main a fixed spoke in the wheel without the opportunities offered here...."[33] Ladd concluded: "Whatever friction there has been is now a thing of the past in my judgement."[34] Ladd was probably right for by the 20th century Shepperd had established a reputation in North Dakota that would have taken long labor to duplicate elsewhere.[35] Shepperd's long experience at the Agricultural College stood him in good stead in most cases. In 1906 he was made dean of the Division of Agriculture with several departments under his control—applied agriculture with himself as head, agronomy with J.C. McDowell at the helm, and animal husbandry with W.B. Richards as instructor. He held the position of dean until 1915 when C.B. Waldron became dean.

In 1918, however, he suffered one of the greatest disappointments of his entire career. In that year, when the position of director of the Experiment Station opened up, he was passed over for the job, although he seemed to have been "the logical man for it." For some period Shepperd again pondered the idea of leaving the institution, but, for a variety of reasons he decided not to do so. In a quite practical sense he decided that he needed the $4,500 a year he and Mrs. Shepperd were paid for their Station and College jobs, and the Shepperds had acquired a considerable amount of Fargo property that had to be managed. Shepperd also found himself liking the new Station director, P.F. Trowbridge, and decided to see if Trowbridge would be fair to his work. Shepperd was made chairman of the Animal Husbandry Department, which gave him control of all College, Station, and Extension work in the field of his primary interest.[36]

There was more than campus politics involved in his failure to be named director of the Station. Edwin F. Ladd was president in 1918 and this should have assured Shepperd's selection. But his old friend Ladd did not appoint him. Shepperd himself believed that the complex state of North Dakota politics "had enough to do with it." He seems to have been conservative politically, and North Dakota at that time was controlled by the Nonpartisan League. Shepperd himself wrote: "It was also known that I am not a Nonpartisan Leaguer and that settled it." Whether he was correct cannot be determined by the historical record, but it is instructive to recall that Ladd ran on the Nonpartisan ticket for the U.S. Senate in 1920, and he was the man ultimately responsible for Shepperd's failure to obtain the directorship.[37]

During the early and middle 1920s, Shepperd seems to have enjoyed his relief from most administrative chores and concentrated mainly on his distinctive style of writing bulletins. He wrote his

brother that he was writing a "lot of odd typed stuff" and he found
it meeting with a "surprisingly good reception." One achievement
that gave Shepperd particular pride was writing an editorial for the
Country Gentleman. Politics reared its head again when Edwin F.
Ladd, now senator from North Dakota, talked of having Shepperd
appointed as assistant U.S. Secretary of Agriculture. Shepperd's wife,
however, punctured that trial balloon while Shepperd was out of
town. It was easy for Dell to dissuade Shepperd, since his brother-
in-law, M.W. Hays, had suffered a breakdown while serving as
assistant Secretary of Agriculture.

In 1928 his alma mater at Ames, Iowa, awarded him an
honorary doctoral degree.[38] Of greater importance, Shepperd was
made acting president of the North Dakota Agricultural College
in September 1928. He became the official president on March 31,
1930.[39] His reaction to the new position was open and refreshing.
He informed his brother: "To be frank with you I like the president
job. I had not realized the power a man in this position has before.
We have a state board here in charge of all penal and charitable
institutions in the state which give them so much (to do) that they
know little of one institution."[40] Shepperd was to be president in
difficult times. The stock market crash, the Depression, and the total
collapse of farm prices coincided almost exactly with the period of
his administration. From the beginning he realized that finances
would be his most difficult responsibility. He wrote: "I do not face
altogether roseate conditions as the finances are in rather bad shape
and popularity and curtailment do not ordinarily go hand in
hand."[41]

But not everything was retrenchment during the Shepperd
presidency. In 1930 he was busily supervising the construction of
two new buildings on the NDAC campus. One was a men's
dormitory that was to cost around $200,000 and later was to be
called Churchill Hall, and the other was a physical education-
auditorium building erected for approximately $210,000. The men's
dormitory was to house 200 students and the auditorium complex,
now the Physical Education Building, would seat 3,600 for a
basketball game and 8,300 for other public occasions.[42]

As the Depression deepened, Shepperd's own economy
measures were matched by those of the 1933 Legislature. The
Legislature was determined to cut salaries, and even facing that
problem, Shepperd was determined that the old foe, the University
of North Dakota, should not do better than the Agricultural College.
He wrote about the University-College rivalry: "I am conceited

enough to think I am holding my own with them. Our tactics are very different. The times are so bad that we will both have a terrible time to live on what we will get."[43] In the midst of the legislative session Shepperd noted that President Kane of the University had resigned and remarked that he was not surprised. Perhaps under the circumstances it was not surprising.[44]

The legislative session turned out even worse than Shepperd feared. His own salary—$7,800 annually—was cut 62 percent. Worse from a morale and institutional point of view were the brutal cuts enforced on faculty and staff. Even taking into account low prices during the Depression, the cuts were severe. Most faculty members could expect reductions of 50 percent or even more. Returning home from Bismarck, Shepperd noted: "The workers on our staff are both peevish and irritable."[45]

Rumors about Shepperd's possible retirement in the mid-30s reached a climax in 1935 when the Associated Press and the *Fargo Forum* not only forecast the 66-year-old Shepperd's retirement, but named his successor, Dr. George Chaney of Des Moines. But the Board of Administration had never discussed Shepperd's retirement and there was absolutely no truth to the story. Perhaps rumbles of discontent caused the story to circulate, but the rumor was soon crushed.[46]

Shepperd's final troubles erupted during the legislative session of 1937 when he was brutally grilled by members of the House Appropriations Committee. Shepperd wrote: "I am just temporarily free from the most fiendish legislative committee I have ever met or in fact any other group.... They have tried to throw me out of the institution and may yet succeed."[47] Still, Shepperd did not fear the outcome either way, since he felt that by age 68 a man's reputation had been either made or lost.[48]

The real motive behind the legislative grilling seems to have been the decision to go over the College books to see if there were any irregularities. The anti-Shepperd members of the Appropriations Committee were actively coached by College Secretary S.W. Hagen. In spite of their efforts, no sign of irregularities were found in college accounts. The psychological effect on Shepperd and his administration, however, was a telling one.[49]

College historian William C. Hunter interpreted Shepperd's fall from power as "a distinct note of censure against him." At the same time Hunter believed President Shepperd's efforts to carry on in spite of economic distress and political opposition should be appreciated.[50] Shepperd himself appraised his record more mundanely. He wrote his brother: "I have removed $175,000 of debt from the College in my eight years in this office. The student attendance is the greatest (1936-37) that the institution has ever known. No red ink on our ledgers. It has been a pinching, saving eight years and the next two will be as bad or worse."[51] It could be argued that Shepperd had attained his goal of fiscal solvency for the College before his resignation.

On March 24, 1937, Shepperd sent the following message to the Board of Administration: "I request to be transferred from the position of President of the College to that of President Emeritus and Associate Husbandman of the College, Station and Extension at a salary of sixty percent of my present compensation, at such time as a suitable successor for the presidency can be secured."[52] Privately, Shepperd felt his age, 69, very keenly and he was "tired of executive work." Also, he wanted to get back to writing full time in his specialty, animal husbandry. He felt: "If I am going to write much, I must be at it."[53] Another recurring theme in his correspondence is his weariness with politics. He wrote: "Politics are rampant in the state."[54]

Shepperd's resignation and its acceptance by the Board opened the gates for Governor William Langer and his associates to attain their ultimate goal—control of the federally funded Experiment Station and Extension Service. No sooner was Shepperd gone than the Board embarked on the "Purge of 1937." Seven members of the Agricultural College's administration and staff were arbitrarily removed from their offices and duties and the position of NDAC president was given to John C. West, president of the University of North Dakota.[55] Secure in his new position Shepperd found time in July to wire the Board in Bismarck asking it to grant a hearing to the dismissed faculty members.[56]

After his retirement as president, Shepperd found himself busy with a number of activities, not excluding reflection. In 1938 he commented on the new president, Frank Lissenden Eversull, by writing: "He is so much better than we expected to get that we feel reasonably well satisfied."[57] Although he had spent 45 years at the College, he wrote that he could not feel conceited about the matter because Dell would not allow it. He was now teaching an introductory course in animal husbandry to young men on relief and found what he called the "folk course" very interesting. He was also involved in writing his tales. He wanted to revise his sheep tales, but found himself handicapped because one of his sources of inspiration was not available. "Daddy" Geiken was ill. Still Shepperd persisted. He declared: "The writing attracts me greatly but it is hard work. It seems like doing something with permanence."[58] He was planning an article on grazing trials at Mandan.[59]

In his last letter to his brother before his unexpected death of pneumonia January 23, 1939, Shepperd wrote of the gift to the college of five horses by a former student. He was continuing in his "folk school" work, but had a few weeks off to concentrate on his writing.[60] The Agricultural College honored his memory in 1942 when it named the newly erected livestock arena for him.[61]

Shepperd served the North Dakota Agricultural College for nearly 46 years in a variety of roles and had concrete accomplishments to his credit. He was not always happy in Fargo, but events and personalities rivetted him to the school and city. But his fame transcended the local area. He was honored by his alma mater, received a gold medal from overseas, and his portrait was hung in the Saddle and Sirloin Club of Chicago in recognition of his work at the International Livestock Exposition in Chicago. Shepperd did important work with plants, but his great love was livestock. Even his plant work was in connection with livestock.

Shepperd taught, did experimental work, and was an administrator on almost all levels, including the presidency of the College. Whether it was the International, the New Salem Breeding Circuit, or local judging contests, Shepperd left his impact on the livestock world of North Dakota. Perhaps his happiest years were the 1920s when he had left behind him the disappointment over the directorship of the Experiment Station and before he was offered the presidency of NDAC. He could study, research, or write without being bothered with details that had always gotten in his way in previous periods. His last months after the presidency also seemed tranquil and satisfying.

The most noteworthy thing about Shepperd, the livestock specialist and agriculturalist, was his singular way of writing up his scientific findings. He had the learning of a scientist, mixed with the soul of a man of letters. Early in his life he tried to stifle his literary bent, but he finally succumbed and used his writing style to put over his scientific points. His bulletins were widely read and his voluminous writings for farm journals reached a wide audience. He reached a sort of apex for his career, or so he thought, when *Country Gentlemen* allowed him to write one of its editorials. Without his literary skills he might have researched as much, but less talent in writing would have deprived that research of its broad impact.

Shepperd was a man of fortunate contrasts. He was well-educated but very practical. He was a shrewd businessman, but business was only a sideline. His letters to his older brother reveal a man who was sensitive and introspective, yet a good judge of people. His long tenure at the Agricultural College gave him a perspective on people and events that could not be matched. His failures seem to have prepared him for future success; he did not become Experiment Station director but he did become NDAC president. He served a young, growing institution in his youth, and guided the same College and Station in its middle years when a depression threatened the very life of the institution. All in all, he was a man of significant accomplishments, but unlike many of the successful, he remained humane and likable.

As a young man John Shepperd enjoyed traveling throughout North Dakota. Here he is riding in the Badlands.

President and Mrs. Shepperd were also world travelers. They are at the center of this group near the Egyptian pyramids.

John Shepperd's term as president from 1929-1937 was a difficult one. After contending with the depressed economic times, and Governor William Langer, Shepperd resigned the presidency and returned to his research at the Experiment Station.

John Henry Shepperd

Footnotes

[1] J.H. Shepperd, "After Forty Years," handed to C.W. Johnson Friday evening, December 29, 1933, for Fargo *Forum* Sunday Issue, Typescript in the John Henry Shepperd Papers, North Dakota Institute for Regional Studies, Fargo, North Dakota. See also W.C. Hunter, *Beacon Across the Prairie: North Dakota's Land Grant College* (Fargo: North Dakota Institute for Regional Studies, 1961), p. 24.

[2] Short Biography of Shepperd, apparently written by Shepperd, Shepperd Papers, NDIRS.

[3] J.H. Shepperd, "Tales of the Early Settlers," *Quarterly Journal* of the University of North Dakota, Vol. 13, No. 3, April, 1923, pp. 268-269.

[4] Short Biography of Shepperd, Shepperd Papers, NDIRS.

[5] "Dr. Shepperd Won International Fame, Developed North Dakota Livestock Industry," Fargo *Forum*, January 23, 1939. Clipping in Masonic Collection, NDIRS.

[6] *Ibid.*

[7] *Ibid.* H.L. Walster, "John Henry Shepperd" in *Five for the Land,* an unpublished manuscript in the holdings of the NDIRS; and Short Biography of Shepperd, Shepperd papers, NDIRS. Robert C. Schectz, registrar, Drake University to author, April 27, 1982.

[8] H.L. Walster, "John Henry Shepperd," NDIRS, and Short Biography, NDIRS. See Earle D. Ross, *The Land-Grant Idea at Iowa State college* (Ames, Iowa: Iowa State College Press, 1958), p. 90. For further confirmation of low enrollment in agriculture, Rackham Holt, *George Washington Carver* (Garden City, New York: Doubleday, Doran and Company, Inc., 1943), p. 73.

[9] H.L. Walster, "John Henry Shepperd," NDIRS.

[10] Dr. Shepperd Won International Fame, Developed North Dakota Livestock Industry," Fargo *Forum* January 23, 1938, and H.L. Walster, "John Henry Shepperd," NDIRS.

[11] H.L. Walster, "John Henry Shepperd," NDIRS, p. 12.

[12] "Dr. Shepperd Won International Fame, Developed North Dakota Livestock Industry," Fargo *Forum* January 23, 1938, and H.L. Walster, "John Henry Shepperd," NDIRS. See also Hunter, *Beacon Across the Prairie*, p. 24.

[13] Dr. Shepperd Won International Fame, Developed North Dakota Livestock Industry," Fargo *Forum* January 23, 1939. Hunter, *Beacon Across the Prairie*, p. 26, for Shepperd's boarding and College Hall's various uses.

[14] J.H. Shepperd, "After Forty Years," NDIRS.

[15] Hunter, *Beacon Across the Prairie*, p. 25 and p. 28.

[16] *Ibid.*

[17] Shepperd, "After Forty Years."

[18] *Ibid.*

[19] Hunter, *Beacon Across the Prairie*, p. 142, and "Mrs. Shepperd, Wife of Late N.D.A.C. President, Dies at 90," no name of paper, September 1, 1954, newspaper clipping in Shepperd Papers. Lewis F. Crawford, *History of North*

Dakota (Chicago: A. Hist. Soc., 1931), p. 17.

[20]Shepperd to J.S. Galesfska, Ardock, North Dakota, August 20, 1902, Shepperd Papers, urging a student to return to school; Shepperd to Thomas Canfield, Lake Park, Minnesota, March 12, 1902, Shepperd Papers for Shepperd seeking employment for a student; Shepperd to ———————, no address, no date, Shepperd Papers for a trip to tour livestock in the Twin Cities area, 30 students to go; and H.L. Walster, "John Henry Shepperd," NDIRS for the "good teacher" judgment.

[21]Barteldes and Company, Colorado Seed House, Denver, Colorado, to Shepperd, August 24, 1901, Shepperd Papers for interest shown in the variety; Shepperd to Northwest Milling Company, Northwood, North Dakota; Shepperd Papers for Shepperd's appointment to the committee; and Shepperd to Professor W.H. Olin, Ft. Collins, Colorado, November 7, 1905, Shepperd Papers, for Shepperd's gratitude that durum wheat now had a better market. David B. Danbom, *The Resisted Revolution: Urban America and the Industrialization of Agriculture 1900-1930* (Ames: Iowa State Univeristy Press, 1979). p. 132. For Carleton's role in discovering the durum consult: Cecil Salmon, USDA, and J. Allen Clark, USDA *Durum Wheat*, USDA Farmers' Bulletin 534, p. 5.

[22]H.L. Walster, "John Henry Shepperd," NDIRS.

[23]H.L. Walster, "John Henry Shepperd," NDIRS, and John Shepperd, "Shepperd Says Pharoah's Dream Fits Case of the Great Plains," newspaper clipping, *Daily Pentagraph and Bulletin*, Bloomington, Illinois, no date on clipping, Shepperd Papers, NDIRS. The Shepperd article is the source for the "fat years" and "lean years" quote.

[24]H.L. Walster, "John Henry Shepperd," NDIRS. J.H. Shepperd, "The Northern Pig From Birth to Market," North Dakota Experiment Station Bulletin, April 1922, p. 3.

[25]John Henry Shepperd to W.B. (Bruce) Shepperd, April 18, 1922, p. 4, in the Shepperd Papers. The John to Bruce Shepperd letters cover the period of time 1918-1938 and are revealing in the extreme. Shepperd lets his older brother Bruce know his inner side and related to him things he would never confide to almost anyone else.

[26]*Ibid.*, See also newspaper clipping, *Daily Pentagraph and Bulletin*, Bloomington, Illinois, Saturday, December 31, 192___ for more information on the story telling.

[27]Consult the Shepperd Papers found in Hultz Hall which are totally about the International Livestock Exposition and Shepperd's involvement in it. See also John Henry Shepperd to W.B. (Bruce) Shepperd, April 3, 1921, NDIRS.

[28]H.L. Walster, "John Henry Shepperd," NDIRS. J.H. Shepperd, "After Forty Years."

[29]H.L. Walster, "John Henry Shepperd," NDIRS.

[30]Hunter, *Beacon Across the Prairie*, p. 51.

[31]*Ibid.*, p. 52.

[32]Edwin F. Ladd to Shepperd, September 18, 1904, Shepperd Papers.

[33]*Ibid.*

[34]*Ibid.*

[35]See the file "Applications for Positions, 1904-1920," Shepperd Papers for Shepperd's various attempts to move. See John A. Craig, dean and director, Texas Agricultural Experiment Station, to Shepperd, June 20, 1904, Shepperd Papers, for Shepperd's desire to move South.

[36]John Shepperd to Bruce Shepperd, August 29, 1918, and John Shepperd to Bruce Shepperd, February 12, 1919, Shepperd Papers, for the information in the above paragraph. Hunter, *Beacon Across the Prairie*, p. 39, p. 90, for the deanship.

[37]John H. Shepperd to Bruce Shepperd, February 12, 1919, Shepperd Papers.

[38]John Shepperd to Bruce Shepperd, October 19, 1923, and John Shepperd to Bruce Shepperd, August 5, 1928, Shepperd Papers.

[39]Hunter, *Beacon Across the Prairie*, pp. 122-123.

[40]John Shepperd to Bruce Shepperd, October 1, 1929, Shepperd Papers.

[41]John Shepperd to Bruce Shepperd, October 1, 1929, Shepperd Papers.

[42]John Shepperd to Bruce Shepperd, March 30, 1930, and John Shepperd to Bruce Shepperd, April 19, 1930, Shepperd Papers.

[43]John Shepperd to Bruce Shepperd, February 29, 1933, Shepperd Papers.

[44]*Ibid.*

[45]John Shepperd to Bruce Shepperd, July 30, 1930, for Shepperd's salary and John Shepperd to Bruce Shepperd, May 9, 1933, for depression time salary cuts. Both letters are in the Shepperd Papers.

[46]John Shepperd to Bruce Shepperd, November 22, 1935, Shepperd Papers.

[47]John Shepperd to Bruce Shepperd, February 20, 1937, Shepperd Papers.

[48]*Ibid.*

[49]Hunter, *Beacon Across the Prairie*, p. 136.

[50]*Ibid.*, p. 142.

[51]John Shepperd to Bruce Shepperd, July 22, 1937, Shepperd Papers.

[52]*Ibid.*

[53]*Ibid.*

[54]*Ibid.*

[55]Hunter, *Beacon Across the Prairie*, p. 144, and John Shepperd to Bruce Shepperd, August 12, 1937, Shepperd Papers.

[56]*Ibid.*, pp. 145-146.

[57]John Shepperd to Bruce Shepperd, October 30, 1938, Shepperd Papers.

[58]John Shepperd to Bruce Shepperd, January 5, 1939, Shepperd Papers.

[59]John Shepperd to Bruce Shepperd, October 30, 1938, Shepperd Papers, and John Shepperd to Bruce Shepperd, August 12, 1938, Shepperd Papers.

[60]John Shepperd to Bruce Shepperd, January 5, 1939, Shepperd Papers.

[61]Hunter, *Beacon Across the Prairie*, p. 201.

Lawrence Root Waldron

Lawrence Root Waldron, Scientist as Wheat Breeder

Lawrence Root "L.R." Waldron, C.B's younger brother, was one of the pioneers in the scientific study of agriculture in North Dakota, first as a student and then as a researcher. Among the problems confronting these agri-scientists were the variable High Plains climate and the leaf and stem rust epidemics that periodically plagued hard red spring wheat in the Upper Great Plains.[1] Waldron, North Dakota Agricultural College's pioneer plant breeder, worked diligently to develop varieties of spring wheat that would withstand those conditions.

Waldron was born near Ionia, Michigan, on October 20, 1875, the son of Mr. and Mrs. Davis S. Waldron.[2] From an early age he was interested in botany and taxonomy. As a high school student he collected plants and once won a prize for his exhibit at the county fair. From early adolescence he studied the natural phenomena related to farming.[3] After high school he taught for two terms at Hardscrabble, Michigan, for $20 a month.[4] While teaching he saved enough money to move to Fargo where his elder brother, Clare Bailey "C.B." Waldron, was teaching at the fledgling North Dakota Agricultural College.[5]

It has been said that Waldron arrived in Fargo in 1896 with $5 in his pocket. Whether that was true or not, it became part of the Agricultural College mythology. In addition to his work of classifying plants for the College Botany Department at 12 or 15 cents an hour, he studied botany under Henry Luke Bolley. Rigorous courses in mathematics, chemistry and biology awaited the eager young man. Waldron's biographer has noted that he was extremely enthusiastic about his courses. His outstanding classroom performance pointed him toward graduate school for which he prepared by including the German language in his program of study. He received his bachelor's in 1899 and was retained as an assistant in botany. The following year he and Bolley compiled the first list of North Dakota plants, which had been started by C.B. Waldron. NDAC botanist O.A. Stevens, who described North Dakota plants in the 1950s, said that Bolley and Waldron had listed about three-fourths of the plants he found growing in North Dakota in the later period. Waldron was also instrumental in building up the herbarium at the College. His diligence as a student and assistant were early indications of the thoroughness that would make him a careful scientist.[6]

Waldron attracted the attention of the faculty while at the University of Michigan where he went to pursue graduate work in 1902. He was offered a stipend larger than many graduate students who had been there for two years.[7] He earned a master's degree in zoology and botany, but he was somewhat undecided which field to specialize in. His master's thesis, accomplished under the direction of Professor Jacob Reigehard, concerned ganoid fish. Reigehard was interested in fish and had been a member of the Michigan Fish Commission. But when Waldron returned to Fargo, he became assistant botanist in the Experiment Station.

Waldron's life was not all work. There was also romance, marriage and family life. In 1903 he was married to Emma Grafenstein of Jamestown, North Dakota. Emma was also a native of Michigan, having been born in Central on September 10, 1875. When she was eight she moved to Jamestown with her parents, Herman and Johanna Grafenstein and lived there until her parents died. She moved to Fargo to make her home with a sister, Mrs. Thomas Hall. Thomas Hall was in the newspaper business at that time, being associated with the *Fargo Argus* and later the *Morning Call*. He was later a congressman from North Dakota. Emma and Waldron were married in the Hall home.[8] To that union were born Heber, Frederick, Charles, Lois, and Ruth Ann.[9]

In 1905 the state Legislature appropriated funds for a branch Experiment Station at Dickinson, a cattle town surrounded by open range, and Waldron took charge as the first superintendent. Interest in a branch station in western North Dakota had dated from 1903 when Bolley had issued a report "Forage and Grass Studies," which noted the need for such a station in the North Dakota ranch country. The *Bismarck Weekly Tribune* approved editorially of Waldron's appointment as superintendent.[10]

Waldron and his assistants were very busy from the start. They broke land and back-set, sowed alfalfa, seeded brome grass, planted a bed of quack grass, seeded macaroni wheats, planted millets and barley, seeded corn, prepared a bed for asparagus, developed rotation plots, cradled wheat, and threshed. Since the branch station was new, it was necessary to dig a well, build a barn, dig post holes, and build a house. Horses had to be obtained, farm machinery acquired, and a windmill repaired. Other activities included hauling manure, poisoning gophers, planting fruit trees, and establishing a Russian olive hedge.[11]

One of Waldron's accomplishments while at Dickinson was to cooperate with Charles J. Brand of the U.S. Department of Agriculture in establishing the hardiness of Grimm alfalfa as compared to other strains.[12] He also became interested in agriculture on the Missouri Slope, a topographical area west of the Missouri River, and his first station bulletin in 1907 was "Hints to Homesteaders." According to one expert, his section on dry-land farming was particularly helpful to farmers.[13] In 1911 Waldron's bulletin on alfalfa appeared, followed in 1912 by a special bulletin on dry farming.[14] Another bulletin covered the question of the effectiveness of bumble bees in fertilizing red clover blossoms. Waldron also found time to arrange the planting of trees and ornamental shrubs at the Dickinson Station.[15] His busy schedule at Dickinson did not mean he had dropped his former interests. He continued to be an enthusiastic plant collector, corresponding with Bolley concerning his finds.[16]

His diaries indicate that the 1905 growing season had ups and downs. In July he exulted about the "wonderful season,"[17] but by September he had to admit the dry weather and hot winds had destroyed the grass plots.[18] In September, however, he noted there was progress on the Station house and the brick work was going along well.[19] By the time he left the Dickinson Station in 1915, it was well established. The Dickinson Station period provided Waldron with the opportunity to be sweeping in his general interests in agriculture. Later in life he would play the role of the more narrow specialist at the Agricultural College.

In the fall of 1915 Waldron presented a paper on alfalfa at the USDA's Northern Great Plains Field Station in Mandan. Thomas Cooper, director of the North Dakota Experiment Station, was so impressed by the paper that he offered Waldron the position of the first plant breeder at North Dakota Agricultural College.[20]

Cooper was an arch conservative in a time of radical ferment in North Dakota. According to Bolley, he was the sworn enemy of E.F. Ladd and President J.H. Worst and himself.[21] There is no written evidence as to how young Waldron handled the tension between Bolley and Cooper, but the fact that he survived indicates that he must have used a considerable amount of finesse in the early days. Waldron accepted the job and remained in that position until the end of his professional career, with the exception of two years during the late 1920s when he left to earn his doctor of philosophy degree in genetics at Cornell.[22]

According to H.L. Walster, Waldron's mission as plant breeder was twofold, first to establish laws of inheritance for plants and second to produce useful new varieties.[23] The theories of genetics were to have a profound effect on Waldron's work. The basic laws of inheritance were first discovered by Gregor Mendel, a monk in a monastery at Brunn in Moravia. He presented his findings in a paper presented to the Natural History Society of Brunn in 1865. His work was published the next year, but little interest was shown in his ideas until the rediscovery of Mendel's laws in 1900. This rediscovery and verification was the work of three European scientists—Correns in Germany, Tschmark in Austria, and DeVries in Holland, working separately, but arriving at similar conclusions almost simultaneously.[24] This was the beginning of the new science of genetics. Mendel's principles have since been shown to apply in a general sense to living things that reproduce sexually. His laws were based on his experiments with the garden pea. Mendel discovered that when peas with different characteristics—say height—were bred, all of the first generation would resemble one of the parents in that characteristic. He called this characteristic dominant. The recessive or hidden characteristic would reappear in the second generation, however, with a ratio of 25 percent dominant, 50 percent hybrid (which would have the appearance of the dominant parent but would carry both dominant and recessive genes) and 25 percent recessive. Modern genetics has modified Mendelism, but the foundation is still basically the same.

Many practitioners of the "new botany" were, however, unwilling to change from their reliance on the survival-of-the-fittest principle to Mendel's genetic principles. As an example, there is no evidence that H.L. Bolley ever adopted Mendelism in his work. Foreign exploration trips by agriculturalists, such as those by USDA botanist Mark A. Carleton and Bolley, though, did give impetus to wheat breeding. Both men brought collections of hard red spring and durum wheat back to North Dakota. The resistance of durum to stem rust during the epidemic of 1904 gave durum a good start in North Dakota.[25] L.R. Waldron's position as plant breeder gave him his first opportunity for in-depth study along specialized lines. He would devote the major part of his effort to breeding rust-resistant varieties of hard red spring wheat.

The earliest known cultivation of wheat in the Red River Valley of the North occurred in 1819 when Lord Selkirk paid 1,000 pounds sterling for 250 bushels of Scotch Fife seed for planting. The next year wheat was sown and harvested in the Valley. The Fife wheats, Red and Power Fife, were the most widely grown varieties until the 1900s and were planted during the Bonanza period.[26]

Waldron's life work was shaped and financed by the periodic leaf and stem rust epidemics that plagued North Dakota wheat farms. Such catastrophes struck in 1904, 1916, 1950, 1953 and 1954, most of them during his professional career. Waldron's successor, Glenn S. Smith, described the epidemics thus: "It is difficult to realize the impact, if you have not experienced it, of this microscopic fungus, the stem rust organism, when a virulent race encounters a susceptible host in combination with favorable winds and humidity."

Disasters of such proportions led to appropriations for wheat variety improvements.[27]

A Canadian wheat, Marquis, proved superior to the commonly grown Fifes and blue stems in such years as 1904 and 1916 when rust was a factor. Marquis was also superior to later-ripening varieties in years experiencing a late summer drought. For these reasons Marquis became the leading hard red spring wheat in North Dakota as well as throughout the hard red spring wheat belt. Marquis was discovered and introduced in 1903 by Dr. Charles E. Sanders of the Central Experiment Farm in Ottawa, Canada.[28]

The research necessary to produce new strains of rust-resistant wheat took years. Waldron had both the patience and the time to produce new varieties of wheat. A devoted scholar, he followed in the Mendel tradition and was well-versed in genetics.

Waldron was ahead of his time in his plot techniques and used the statistical approach. The lattice design of his experiments was the methodology he would use in developing new strains of wheat for the region[29] and it is still considered good practice today.

Waldron's first attempt at wheat improvement was through crosses to improve Marquis. In 1916 Waldron and J. Allen Clark of the U.S. Department of Agriculture observed that a new wheat from Bolley's collection was one of the few unaffected varieties in that terrible rust year. They named this wheat Kota, for North Dakota, and from Marquis crossed with Kota Waldron produced Ceres.

Ceres, released in 1926, was an earlier maturing variety than Marquis and was more drought and rust resistant. Ceres came to be seeded in 4 million acres in spring wheat country and each year gave an important dividend over Marquis. One authority states that Ceres was the first hybrid spring wheat produced in the United States. This probably was not true. As early as 1916 crosses were made that led to the variety Marquillo at the University Farm in St. Paul, Minnesota. Marquillo was distributed in 1928. But the fact that regional experts felt Ceres was first is indicative of Waldron's stature in the field and area.[30] A variety from the same cross as Ceres, Komar, was grown in Iowa, Nebraska, South Dakota and Colorado.

Waldron's next significant variety, Rival, had a more sophisticated pedigree, being Ceres crossed with Hope-Florence. Hope was a South Dakota wheat and Florence came from Australia. Rival was a higher-yielding variety and was resistant to stem rust race 56, which had destroyed Ceres in 1935. Rival was more susceptible to lodging, black chaff and to shattering, but growers preferred it, maintaining that they could still harvest more grain with Rival than with other varieties. Rival was distributed in 1939.[31]

Glenn Smith believed that Mida was Waldron's outstanding wheat. It was released in 1944, and in 1949 it was planted in 5.5 million acres in North Dakota. To achieve Mida, Waldron crossed a sib of Rival with a breeding line from Canada, L.I. 625. Mida had a large kernel that would withstand weathering. It also had a vigorous growth habit, wide adaptability, resistance to heat, and was satisfactory in quality and high in yield. Mida's higher yield gave about a two-bushel advantage in normal years and a larger advantage in rust years.[32] Mida wheat, incidentally, was named for Mrs. Ida B. Prokop of Lidgerwood, North Dakota, who sculpted busts of both L.R. Waldron and his brother C.B. Waldron.[33] It is important to emphasize that the production of Mida, and later varieties, did not mean the abandonment of grains made in the development of Ceres.

One measurement by which Waldron's work can be evaluated is the acreage of his varieties grown in a given year. In 1949, long after its prime, Ceres was still grown on more than 600,000 acres. This was, of course, down from a high of 4 million acres before Ceres was "taken out" by a stem rust epidemic in 1935. That the variety lasted so long and was still preferred by farmers is an indication that Ceres was a strong and enduring variety.[34] Rival, Waldron's second variety, was still being grown on nearly 3 million acres as late as 1949. The severe rust epidemic of 1953-1954 was surely the reason for its decline to somewhat more than 400,000 acres in 1954. Still, Rival had endured a long time because of the number of stem and leaf rust epidemic years it had survived and in spite of the competition of the superior Mida.[35] Mida, undoubtedly Waldron's chief contribution to the wheat industry, hit its peak in 1949 with

5.5 million acres. Its decline was brought on by the stem rust problem of 1953-1954. Thus near the end of his career, Waldron found his varieties still acceptable on many Northern Great Plains farms.[36] Reflecting on his career late in life Waldron observed: "...when some success had been attained along would come something, a new strain of rust, to bring disaster. This happened to Ceres with stem rust and later to Rival and Mida, with leaf rust. But the greatest disaster was this newest invasion of '15B.' "[37]

The effect of this new rust strain, which struck in 1950, was indeed devastating. Several factors combined to make 15B deadly, among them a very late spring and slow development of crops generally.[38]

Concerned though he might have been with this particular epidemic, Waldron was still more concerned about the origin of the rust. He wrote: "...for me I'd be too non-human to let it pass unnoticed when millions (of dollars) of damage could have been averted with reasonable care. Also, I am personally much concerned as you can well imagine—to see valuable varieties damned into oblivion."[39]

Despite these problems near the end of his career, Waldron was not prepared to give up in the 1950s what he could not have abandoned in the 1920s or 1930s. In his last bulletin he stated: "...widespread appearance in 1950 of the relatively new race of stem rust of wheat, 15B, had developed difficult problems. Our present ignorance of how this new form is going to behave adds to our difficulty..."[40] He concluded: "This season, 1951, will probably tell whether progress can be made against 15B."[41]

To meet the challenge of 15B, Waldron began a series of crosses between Mida and Lee, a Minnesota variety. Minnesota Lee had emerged with much less damage than other varieties in 1953, but by 1954 it, too, was being severely attacked in some places. The 15B crisis became apparent in 1950 when even highly rust-resistant durums succumbed.[42] A dedicated scientist, Waldron took the long view. He wrote: "Out of the ruins of past disasters, new values have been developed for the future."[43]

During his entire professional life, Waldron's attention and delight in his family persevered. On Christmas Day 1921 he noted in his diary: "Usual Christmas doings. Children had tree and plenty of presents. Charles acted as Santa Claus. Star cakes, corn flakes, decorated cookies, etc., for breakfast. We all went to C.B.'s for Christmas dinner where we had turkey, etc. Emma made pumpkin pie and biscuits. Played one game cards. Very pleasant day."[44] Of special note was his fraternal devotion to his older brother, C.B.

His 1923 diary contains the story of his son Heber's bout with typhoid. Waldron wrote: "Slept on floor in Heber's room. Had him taken to St. Luke's hospital at 9:30. Called there in p.m. twice and again after supper. He is pretty sick but should pull through."[45] The illness was a long one but finally Waldron was able to write: "Brought Heber home from hospital after 40 days. Got him home safely with no indication of temperature. Certainly much of a relief."[46] His family remained central in Waldron's life.

His diary for 1925 reveals an extremely busy professional man who still found time for other activities. He was a member of the Plymouth Congregational Church, belonging to that church's men's club and serving as church treasurer for a time. He had various financial interests in Fargo and kept up with such matters on a regular basis. Possibly his favorite part-time activity was gardening. From hoeing through canning he kept busy supplying a good deal of his family's food. Crossword puzzles were one of his interests, and he found time to read poetry to Ruth Ann.[47]

As the years went by, Waldron became more reflective. At the time of his 50th birthday in 1925 he wrote: "Well, here I am at the mid-century mark, beginning, I suppose to get old. What have I accomplished for the world and for myself? Ceres wheat the greatest accomplishment? I don't know. Once I thought that at this state I would be really old."[48] He ended on a philosophical note: "Well, I must continue to take care of myself."[49]

The year 1926 found Waldron more exuberant. Writing in his diary he said: "The time will come when the main wheat acreage of N.D. will be planted to these hybrids. Speed the day."[50] Thus he could look to the future with his solid accomplishments forever on the horizon. His love of family continued unabated. At one point he wrote: "Read to Ruth Ann about 'an old, old, old, old lady and a boy who was 1/2 past 3' and she liked it very much."[51]

In 1927 Waldron noted that rust was still a deadly problem, but he was sure his hybrids could withstand the onslaught. He wrote proudly of his Bison variety: "It is strikingly better than Ceres—whiter and better texture. This is a strikingly promising wheat and could bring me fame—and a pension."[52] He noted that he had done much work on his dwarf material and intended finishing his Ph.D. soon. On the home front Heber turned 21 in 1927 and Ruth Ann suffered through the mumps.[53] 1928 was a banner year for Waldron. In the spring he received his long-sought Ph.D. from Cornell, which provided another recognition of his competence and added another, and much needed, earned doctorate to the faculty. His thesis explored the inheritance of dwarfness in common wheat after crosses have been made among certain varieties. The work was considered pioneering but not definitive.[54] Waldron also served the College through his activities in the Alumni Association, of which he was president of the executive committee in 1928.[55]

Waldron wrote in the 1930s of the success of his children even during the Depression. In 1938 three of them found jobs. Frederick traveled to Egypt to work with an oil company, Charles secured a civil service job with the New Deal tree planting project, and Lois, who had finished library school, became librarian at the State School of Science in Wahpeton. Heber at that time was in Valley City, and Ruth Ann was a student at the Agricultural College and helping with housework.[56] In that year the Waldron household was disturbed when Emma underwent a major—albeit successful—operation.[57]

By 1941 Waldron was increasingly disturbed by the world situation. He anxiously followed the Russo-German conflict and the increasing tension with Japan. When the actual war came on December 7, 1941, he merely noted: "Kaltenborn's surmise came true. Japan started attack on Honolulu at 8:00 a.m."[58]

Waldron was noted as the greatest user of the campus library, and it was believed that he had read more books than anyone on the faculty.[59] At one time he appeared on a local radio show "Stump the Professor."[60] When reading in his own field he was apt to fill the margins with penciled notations when he found errors or doubtful statements. His reading, which was broad, included evolution, the Middle Ages, sorcery, the Inquisition, and witchcraft.[61] In 1935 Blue Key fraternity honored him with its Doctor of Service award and in 1944 A.M. Christensen of Minot, North Dakota, presented the College with a bronze bust of Waldron and H.L. Bolley.[62]

Waldron was a member of Sigma Xi and of the Royal Microscope Society of London. One of his most signal honors came when he was made a member of the Linnean Society of London. The society, named for Carolus Linneas, the great Swedish botanist and father of taxonomy, was founded in 1788 when it received its first charter from King George III. It was the first scientific association to be given a royal charter. On Waldron's election in 1933, the Society had only 15 American scientists as members.[63] When the announcement came about the Linnean Society, the Agricultural College tendered Waldron a dinner to signify its appreciation of the great honor.[64]

But as a long-time student and staff member of the North Dakota Agricultural College, Waldron felt he had received no substantial token of approval from his own institution. He wrote, near the end of his career: "The institution has in different years recognized individuals with honorary degrees and otherwise for some outstanding work. When this happened 3 years ago, when my sole classmate here at the AC, back in 1899, was acclaimed by our president I felt fed up. I told Director Walster that for my extensive breeding work the institution has never given me the least public recognition..."[65] Waldron added that since this was a mere factual statement there was nothing for Walster to do but acknowledge its truth.[66] Ruminating on the subject, he declared: "Recognition had come from other sources but the college itself had remained strangely negligent."[67] In addition, he was aggrieved to find his salary declining as a result of near retirement status.[68]

Waldron had clearly developed characteristics of chronic discontent by the 1950s. How much of his attitude was justified and how much was end-of-career grousing is hard to say. He had developed, in the course of his life's work, three major varieties of hard red spring wheat. These varieties bore the brunt of succeeding rust epidemics and put cash in farmers' overalls and a healthy surplus in the state treasury. How much this meant in terms of dollars, one can only estimate. Waldron himself said: "...It is a fact the increased state income from the locally bred varieties has been sufficient to pay our state debt several times over."[69]

His successor, Glenn Smith, put it differently: "...a little arithmetic will reveal that the work of this one scientist, creating new wheat varieties, has saved North Dakota more than the total cost of all appropriations for N.D.S.U. in the 75 historical years of its existence."[70]

To estimate the economic benefits of Waldron's breeding work would require virtually another book. In one approach it would be necessary to determine the return on alternate varieties and crops as well as the effect on the price both of North Dakota production of alternatives and the effect of Waldron's successes on the price of wheat. Another approach involves a fairly sophisticated statistical estimate of the value of research. Without such an estimate, all that can safely be said is that Waldron's wheat breeding helped to keep North Dakota farmers raising substantial crops of wheat. This crop, in the absence of the threat of rust, had proven the best adapted to the soil, climate, and situation of the farmers.[71]

The complexity of modern wheat breeding is nowhere better illustrated than in the pedigrees of Waldron's varieties and their successors. Viewed from this standpoint, Waldron's varieties still have an important impact on hard red spring wheat grown in the Upper Midwest. As an example, in 1969 the North Dakota State University Department of Agronomy released its new hard red spring wheat variety Waldron, which was named in honor of L.R. Waldron. Developing Waldron required a sequence of four separate North Dakota crosses. The first cross, Lee with Mida, was under study by Waldron when he retired in 1953. On the Justin side of Waldron's pedigree, Mida also entered into its parentage.[72] The ultimate variety, Waldron, represented 16 generations of work in ten years.[73]

L.R. Waldron's sophisticated and productive work was made possible not only by his dedication and ability but by the work of others. He benefited from the rediscovery of Mendel's law and from the travels and collections of colleagues—those of Bolley in particular. He also benefited from the coincidence of rust epidemics and new appropriations that made possible his specialization in breeding.

Waldron's first phase as a scientist was that of student, assistant and superintendent of the Dickinson sub station. At the sub station he was concerned with many problems of agriculture in the Northern Great Plains, focusing on dry-land farming, alfalfa growing, and horticulture. The second period of his career was that of the first specialist in plant breeding at the Agricultural Experiment Station in Fargo. Here, with time out for graduate training in genetics, he spent the rest of his life trying to develop higher-yielding varieties of hard red spring wheat that would be resistant to stem and leaf rust. He benefited most from that opportunity to specialize. Coming to the Agricultural College later than Ladd and Bolley, Waldron benefited from having greater scientific knowledge, which he applied to agricultural problems. This is in no way derogatory to Ladd or Bolley, since their scientific and agricultural accomplishments were great and unique.

His greatest accomplishment was the production of three new, major wheat varieites that could produce in the face of prevalent rust races. In doing this in one lifetime, he displayed a type of toughness not found among other researchers. Faced with the menace of 15B in the early 1950s and with his imminent retirement and death, he talked about "past disasters leading to present triumphs."

He would have liked to have known that his work had endured.

An institution that seldom acknowledged him during his lifetime erected a building named in his honor as well as that of his brother. After his death in 1954, his work was carried on. Waldron, the new North Dakota wheat entry in 1969, carried Mida lineage on both sides of its family tree.[74] Agronomists of today owe much to their hardy predecessors, L.R. Waldron among them.

L.R. Waldron was a graduate of the NDAC class of '99. He joined
the faculty that year. Waldron received a doctorate from Cornell and
served as superintendent of the Dickinson Experiment Station from
1905-16 before returning to the Fargo campus.

L.R. Waldron is best known for breeding rust-resistant wheat
varieties such as Ceres, Rival and Mida.

L.R. Waldron retired from the NDAC faculty in 1952. Sculptor Ida Prokop Lee made busts of Waldron, his brother C.B. and Henry Bolley in 1944.

L.R. Waldron was a recognized scientist with a membership in the Linnaen Society of London. In 1954 Waldron planned the wheat breeding program so ably continued by his successor Glenn Smith.

Lawrence Root Waldron

Footnotes

[1]Howard Roberts Lamar, *Dakota Territory, 1861-1889: A Study in Politics* (New Haven: Yale University Press, 1956), p. 73 for the attitude of settlers toward farming. For a description of the climatic condition of the northern Great Plains see Elwyn B. Robinson, *History of North Dakota* (Lincoln: University of Nebraska Press, 1966). William C. Hunter, *Beacon Across the Prairie* (Fargo: North Dakota Institute for Regional Studies, 1961) adequately surveys the early history of the North Dakota Agricultural College.

[2]Fargo *Forum*, August 22, 1954. This is a comprehensive obituary and biography.

[3]*Ibid.*

[4]*Ibid.*

[5]Erling Nicolai Rolfsrud, *Lanterns Over the Prairies*, Book II (Brainerd, Minnesota: Lakeland Press, 1950), p. 98, and Glenn S. Smith, "Dr. L.R. Waldron: Devoted Wheat Researcher,"*North Dakota Farm Research* Bimonthly Bulletin, Vol. 26, No. 3, January-February 1969, p. 3.

[6]Earl Tweit, "The Work of L.R. Waldron," term paper, fall 1960, Plant Breeding 407, North Dakota State University.

[7]Rolfsrud, *Lanterns*, pp. 98-99; H.L. Walster, "Remarks on Occasion of Dinner Rendered to C.I. Nelson, Bacteriologist, and L.R. Waldron, Plant Breeder," April 29, 1954; and H.L. Walster, "In Honor of Lawrence Root Waldron," Address given July 19, 1954. L.R. Waldron to J.W. Blankinship, Bozeman, Montana, May 10, 1901. H.L. Walster was the longtime dean of agriculture at the North Dakota Agricultural College. See also excerpts of Waldron's letters to H.L. Bolley while he was a graduate student at the University of Michigan, 1901-1902, for his thoroughness as a student. Letters in files of the North Dakota Institue for Regional Studies. For Waldron's overall study program see H.L. Walster, "Lawrence Root Waldron, Plant Breeder" in *Five for the Land*, p. 2, unpublished manuscript in the holdings of the North Dakota Institute for Regional Studies.

[8]Fred Waldron interview.

[9]Fargo *Forum* August 24, 1954, clipping in L.R. Waldron Papers, NDIRS.

[10]H.L. Walster, "Lawrence Root Waldron," p. 5.

[11]L.R. Waldron, *Diary*, 1905.

[12]Rolfsrud, *Lanterns*, p. 99.

[13]Bulletin No. 74, Dickinson Sub-Experiment Station Bulletin No. 1, The assessment was by Walster in "In Honor of Lawrence Waldron," p. 4.

[14]Bulletins 95 and 196 and H.L. Walster, "In Honor," pp. 4-5.

[15]Reported in First Annual Report of the Dickinson Station and Walster, "In Honor of L.R. Waldron," p. 5, and Glenn S. Smith, "Dr. L.R. Waldron: Devoted Wheat Researcher," p. 3.

[16]L.R. Waldron to Bolley, July 17, 1906, Bolley papers, NDIRS.

[17]L.R. Waldron to Bolley, July 16, 1905, Bolley papers, NDIRS.

[18]L.R. Waldron to Bolley, Bolley Papers, NDIRS. No date given, probably September.

[19]L.R. Waldron to Bolley, September 10, 1915, Bolley papers, NDIRS.

[20]Bolley to M.L. Wilson, Bozeman, Montana, January 28, 1916, Bolley papers, NDIRS.

[21]*Ibid.*

[22]Walster, "Lawrence Root Waldron, p. 15.

[23]*Ibid.*

[24]Walster, "In Honor of L.R. Waldron," p. 5.

[25.]Walster, "Lawrence Root Waldron," p. 17.

[26]Glenn S. Smith, "Shaping the Staff of Life," Faculty Lecture, NDSU, p. 17.

[27]*Ibid.*, pp. 16-17, and Hiram Drache, *The Day of the Bonanza: A History of Bonanza Farming in the Red River of the North* (Fargo: NDIRS, 1964), p. 5.

[28]Smith, "Staff of Life," pp. 17-18.

[29]*Ibid.*, pp. 17-20.

[30]T.E. Stoa, *The Agronomy Department*, p. 6. A.H. Reginald Butler, *Essays on Wheat* (New York: The Macmillan Company, 1919), p. 151.

[31]Interview with Glenn S. Smith, November 2, 1976.

[32]Smith, "Staff of Life," p. 18; Walster, "In Honor of L.R. Waldron," p. 6, and "Breeding of Common Wheat Since 1916 at the North Dakota Agricultural Experiment Station," p. 1.

[33]Smith, "Staff of Life," pp. 18-19, and Waldron, "In Honor of L.R. Waldron," p. 7.

[34]North Dakotan, September 1944, p. 4.

[35]Smith, "Staff of Life," pp. 18-19.

[36]S.C. Salmon and L.P. Reitz, Field Crop Research Branch, Agricultural Research Service, *Distribution of the Varieties and Classes of Wheat in the United States in 1954* (U.S. Department of Agriculture, Agricultural Handbook No. 108), p. 12.

[37]*Ibid.*, and Glenn S. Smith, "Dr. L.R. Waldron: Devoted Wheat Researcher," *North Dakota Far Research* (Fargo, NDSU Experiment Station, January 1969), Vol. 26, No. 3, p. 3.

[38]Salmon and Reitz, *Distribution*, p. 12, and Smith, "Dr. L.R. Waldron," p. 3.

[39]L.R. Waldron to Dr. J.B. Harrington, Department of Field Husbandry, University of Saskatchewan, Saskatoon, Canada, undated and carbon copy.

[40]Stoa, *The Agronomy Department*, p. 27.

[41]Waldron to Harrington, no date given.

[42]Fargo *Forum*, August 24, 1954.

[43]*Ibid.*

[44]L.R. Waldron, *Diary*, December 27, 1921.

[45]L.R. Waldron, *Diary*, August 8, 1923.

[46]*Ibid.*, September 27, 1923.

[47]L.R. Waldron, *Diary*, 1925.

[48]L.R. Waldron, *Diary*, October 20, 1925.

[49]*Ibid.*

[50]L.R. Waldron, *Diary*, September 9, 1926.

[51]L.R. Waldron, *Diary,* October 18, 1926.

[52]L.R. Waldron, *Diary,* 1927, and for the direct quote, *Ibid.,* January 14, 1927.

[53]L.R. Waldron, *Diary,* 1927.

[54]T.W. Thordarson, "Plant Wizard Receives Ph.D," *College and State,* March 1928, pp. 9-10.

[55]*College and State,* December 1928, p. 17.

[56]L.R. Waldron, *Diary,* December 31, 1941.

[57]*Ibid.,* March 7, 1938.

[58]L.R. Waldron, *Diary,* December 7, 1941.

[59]Fargo *Forum,* August 24, 1954.

[60]Rolfsrud, *Lanterns,* p. 97.

[61]Fargo *Forum,* August 24, 1954.

[62]Rolfsrud, *Lanterns,* p. 101.

[63]*Ibid.,* pp. 100-101.

[64]Leon Metzinger, chairman of Committee to Dear Colleague, April 7, 1933, L.R. Waldron Papes, NDIRS.

[65]Waldron to Harrington, no date given.

[66]*Ibid.*

[67]*Ibid.*

[68]*Ibid.*

[69]*Ibid.*

[70]Smith, "Staff of Life," p. 19.

[71]*Ibid.*

[72]*Ibid.,* p. 20.

[73]Smith, "Waldron—A New High-Yielding HRS Wheat," *Farm Research Bimonthly Bulletin,* Vol. 26, No. 3, p. 4.

[74]*Ibid.*

Horace Stockbridge

Conclusion

The *Encyclopedia Brittanica* states: "North Dakota State University of Agriculture and Applied Science (established in Fargo as a college in 1890) is a noted centre of agricultural research."[1] That this was true starting with the administration of Horace Edward Stockbridge in 1890, is one of the contentions of this writer. Five extraordinary individuals—C.B. Waldron, H.L. Bolley, Edwin F. Ladd, John H. Shepperd, and later L.R. Waldron—were involved in creating this institution, but it was Stockbridge who gave it its original impetus. Stockbridge was a German-trained Ph.D. in chemistry and as president of NDAC he carefully selected his staff and set high standards of research and teaching for them. Few land grant institutions had a leader of such caliber at their founding. And even fewer had a leader trained in an agriculturally related field.

To give some examples of this, Michigan State College's first president was Joseph R. Williams, who was a lawyer, merchant, miller, editor, and gentleman farmer. He was a Harvard graduate, but his agricultural connections were almost nil.[2] The University of Minnesota, which was a multi-purpose university with an attached agricultural college, naturally had a non-agriculturalist as its first president. He was mathematician William Watts Falwell.[3] The first president at Iowa State was Adonjah Strong Welch, who was born in Connecticut, graduated from the University of Michigan and served as a Reconstruction senator from Florida. He was both a teacher and a dabbler in law and politics but his accomplishments were not in science or farming.[4]

When William C. Hunter was writing his history of the North Dakota Agricultural College he wanted to give it the subtitle *Political Football* rather than *Beacon Across the Prairie*. People close to Hunter and the overall story of the College and Experiment Station have related to this writer that the professor was excessively bitter. Still, the political factor in this academic chronicle cannot be put down. North Dakota politics have been turbulent and at times cruel and almost vicious. The life stories of these men and their original administrator were vitally affected by that fact.

If there is one key to understanding North Dakota history and politics it is the struggle between agrarian radicalism and conservative urban and out-of-state interests. Even before statehood Dakota Territory was the scene of a successful farm rebellion led by the powerful Dakota Farmer's Alliance. In 1892 this agrarian and social movement triumphed with the election of the Populist governor of North Dakota Eli C.D. Shortridge. The triumphant Populists, in the person of Shortridge, moved to take control of the North Dakota Agricultural College in the interests of the farmers. But when Shortridge attempted to remove conservatives from the Board of Trustees, board members fought back. Shortridge was a one-term governor, and when the dust settled the institution had lost its outstanding young president.

Some of President Stockbridge's academic qualifications have been enumerated, but it is important to point out that his high caliber was acknowledged both nationally and internationally. Before 1890 he had been a chemical adviser to the Japanese government and director of the Indiana Experiment Station. He attracted capable young professionals to his embryo staff at NDAC, he carefully planned and ordered research potentially valuable to North Dakota, and he had given every indication that he would mature on the job. While he was succeeded by capable men such as James Buel Power and John H. Worst, no succeeding president of NDAC even approached his qualifications until the 1920s. He was the political victim of the choppy public affairs of an emerging commonwealth and the institution he had headed suffered in consequence.

Clare Bailey "C.B." Waldron also found himself tossed around by the political as well as academic and professional needs of the institution he served as its first paid employee. First retained as the College and Station botanist, he found himself relegated to the less prestigious position as horticulturalist. That field was just emerging as a scientific field, while botany was already regarded as a profession. That event set the tone for the rest of Waldron's career at the College and Station. He became the institution's entomologist, he was dean of agriculture, and he even served as forester in a state with little natural forest. He was in reality the College and Station's handy man. Whether he resented that role is not known.

Henry Luke Bolley survived more storms and flak than the others. The "Hearing of 1916" is well known, but there were other incidents. The best known of these was the rather casual dropping of Bolley as seed commissioner. The professor suffered from the slings and arrows of his conservative opponents, but his overall personal characteristics made his situation worse. Bolley was regarded as eccentric, and even his remarkable scientific achievements did not shield him adequately. His independence, his outspoken ways, and his lack of tact—all contributed to making him a storm center. As an example, during the 1920s, a conservative period in North Dakota, he was interviewed by Upton Sinclair for a work titled *The Goose-Step: A Study of American Education*. Sinclair's work had a left-wing tinge, and it covered among other things John H. Worst's fall and the survival of Edwin F. Ladd. Bolley was, perhaps, indiscreet in his remarks to Sinclair. He speculated: "Maybe it will be my fate to be kicked out for talking to Upton Sinclair!" More important, he ruminated on a philosophical question for college teachers that has never been resolved. He asked: "Is a college professor a citizen? Or does he part with his rights and become some kind of subject when he takes a college job?...I was going to stay a citizen." Maybe this was rash, maybe it was a mistake; certainly it was not good politics.

Of the five men studied in this volume, only Edwin F. Ladd remained unscathed in the political environment. While a liberal, and perhaps even a radical, he learned to turn the machinations of his political foes into personal triumphs. Working from a pure food crusade platform he parlayed himself into something of a folk hero, was victorious when Worst fell under conservative attack, and became a U.S. senator with the support of the radical Nonpartisan League.

Ladd and Bolley suffered because of their liberalism, but John H. Shepperd, ironically enough, had troubles because of conservatism at a time when the College and Station were in liberal, or radical, hands. He was passed over for director of the Experiment Station when Ladd was president probably because Ladd was Nonpartisan League and Shepperd was not. As a younger man, he was a chronic malcontent, always looking for new positions. He often held secondary administrative posts, but never top posts until the troubled 1930s when he was president of the College. Then he was past his prime and although he did a remarkably good job, he did not have enough stamina to survive events leading to the 1930s purge.

Lawrence Root "L.R." Waldron, like his older brother, C.B., suffered from the academic and scientific politics of the institution. Highly specialized, very successful in his wheat breeding, he nevertheless felt the pinch of his low salary and the paucity of public recognition of his life accomplishments. Perhaps his successor Glenn Smith is correct in pointing out that public awards were rare in those simpler years. As for the low salary, L.R. was not alone there. The entire academic community, even as late as the 1950s, suffered from low pay. L.R., at least, had the satisfaction of specializing along one line.

From the beginning of its existence the North Dakota agricultural college and its founders went against the prevailing attitudes of their constituents. The Fargo community really did not want an agricultural college; it wanted something it could appreciate as big and important. If Fargoans had to have something agricultural, they would have appreciated an Experiment Station far more—it would at least have brought in federal monies. But the founders of the institution wanted to create a college specifically for farm youths of both sexes. When he was recalling the early days, C.B. Waldron remembered not only the College's technical and scientific courses, but also the liberal and broadening materials put before the students. He wrote that in one year an instructor might be expected to expound on the starry heavens, on the doings of the Greeks, Romans, Dutch, and Irish, on equations, and on writers and orators moving the multitudes. In other words, the founders did not aim to establish a narrow agricultural college, but one dispensing a broad variety of liberal education courses. Moving in that direction they encountered the bitter enmity of their neighbor down river and their critics who wanted to narrowly define their mission.

A brief survey of one discipline the author knows best, history, might illustrate the concern the Agricultural College had for liberal education courses. History was always taught at NDAC, but in 1898 an historian as such was added to the faculty. His name was A.T. Mills and he was the proud possessor of a bachelor of philosophy degree. Mills' title was instructor of history and civil government. The institution never reversed itself and continued to offer the discipline. By the academic year 1903-1904, there existed at NDAC a Department of History and Civil Government. In 1910 the department boasted its first doctor of philosophy faculty member, Professor W.J. Trimble. Gradually the practice developed of having one doctoral member of the department and one non-doctoral instructor. At least one of the early instructors went on to become an outstanding authority in his reseach field. That was Earle Dudley Ross, who leaving North Dakota went to Iowa State College and became noted for his historical writing on the land grant system.

Following Dr. Horace Stockbridge's tenure as president in 1893, the Agricultural College did not have a president holding a doctoral degree until the 1920s when John Lee Coulter became president. He, among other things, took on the mission to make the College "more like an agricultural college." But the formal motto of the institution was "the state is our campus" and the number of students enrolled in non-agricultural courses outnumbered those in strictly agricultural subjects. This precipitated a student-led movement to change the institution's name from North Dakota Agricultural College to North Dakota State College. In the 1920s, too, the traditional role of the History Department continued. In 1924 Rudolf Ottersen came to the department with a bachelor's degree and became the instructor. In the same year W.C. Hunter arrived with a doctoral degree from Princeton, where, he proudly related, he had studied under Woodrow Wilson. So the tradition of a broadly based curriculum continued, often with fierce opposition from within and without, but by the 1960s the institution was ready to bear the proud title of University.

The five academic scientists whose stories appear on these pages, with the exception of L.R. Waldron, all participated widely in the triangle of the land grant system—teaching, research, and extension. In addition, they helped through administration to give the institution a rational order and coherence. It might be argued that the four were a "new middle class...who developed administration and management" in order to cope with 20th century problems.[5] It was these five, and others, who gave rationality to, and made growth possible for the Agricultural College before the days of professional administrators.

Determining the worth of these men to the institution and state over a period from 1890 to the 1950s leads to the conclusion that the College and Station and North Dakota would not be what they are today without their efforts. If wheat, flax, sugarbeets, livestock, insect control, potatoes, public health, and natural beauty are important to this society, then so were these men. It is not necessary to put a monetary value on their endeavors; it is enough to contemplate the staggering loss to this commonwealth had these men not been a part of its early development. Each one, and they varied in their approach and specialization, did enough to be worth not just millions of dollars to the state today, but to be valued in the hundreds of millions of dollars. Theirs was a monumental accomplishment.

Footnotes

[1]*Encyclopedia Britanica, Micropedia* (Chicago: University of Chicago, 1985).

[2]Madison Kuhn, *Michigan State: The First Hundred Years* (Lansing: The Michigan State University Press, 1955), pp. 16-17.

[3]E. Bird Johnson, Editor, *Forty Years of the University of Minnesota* (Minneapolis: The General Alumni Association, 1910), p. 31.

[4]Earle Dudley Ross, *The Land-Grant Idea at Iowa State College: A Centennial Trial Balance, 1858-1958* (Ames: The Iowa State College Press, 1958), p. 45.

[5]David Donald, From the Forward of Robert H. Wiebe, *The Search for Order, 1877-1920* (New York: Hill and Wang, 1976).

A

Abbott, George Alonzo, 79
AC Mill, 83, 84
Adams Act, 29
Adams, President John Quincey, 9
Agassiz, Louis, 3, 26
Agriculture and Statistical Bureau, 9, 10
Agricultural Museum, 4
Alumni Association (NDAC), 131
American Breeder's, 16
American Breeder's Association, 16
American Federation of Teachers, 64
Americany Lyceum Movement, 1
American Philosophical Society, 4
American Pomological Society, 31
American Seed Trade Association, 59
American Society of Horticulture, 31
Amidon, Charles F., 79, 82
Arthur, J.C., 47, 48, 65, 66
Arvold, Alfred G., 88
Association of Agricultural Chemists, 15, 85
Association of State and National Food and Dairy Departments, 85
Aubert, Alfred, 77

B

Babcock, Stephen M., 78, 108
Bailey, Liberty Hyde, 15, 16, 26, 27, 28, 35
Bakewell, Robert, 3
Beacon Across the Prairie, 67, 143
Beal, W.J., 26
Beecher, Catherine, 1
Bessey, Charles E., 26, 48
Better Farming Association, 62, 63
Bismarck Tribune, 124
Bison (wheat), 130
bleached flour, 83
Blue Key Doctor of Service, 131
blue stem (wheat) 58, 127

Board of Trustees (NDAC), later Board of Administration, 14, 15, 23, 25, 31, 49, 60, 63, 64, 86, 87, 88, 107, 112, 113, 144
Bolley, Ann, Don (children of H.L.), 51, 55
Bolley, Henry Luke, 11, 15, 16, 23, 26, 28, 30, 35, 47-75, 78, 85, 87, 92, 109, 123, 125, 126, 132, 133, 143, 144
Bolley, Mrs. Henry Luke, also see Frances Sheldon (1) and Emily Sheldon (2), 51, 55,
Bolley, John and Mary, 47
Bonanza period, 13, 14
Brand, Charles J., 125
Brannon, M.A., 49, 51
Brewer, W.H., 103
Buchanan, President James, 2, 8, 9
Burbank, Luther, 15, 26
Burke, Governor John, 31
Burnett, E.A., 65
Bussey, Benjamin, 3

C

Cashel, John J., 59
Capper, Arthur, 91
Carleton, Mark A., 11, 16, 84, 106, 126
Carver, George Washington, 104
Ceres (wheat), 58, 84, 127, 128, 129, 130
Chaney, George, 112
Chicago Exposition, 35
Christensen, A.M., 131
Christian, George C., 13
Christiansen, John, 106, 107
Churchill, O.O., 30
Churchill Hall, 111
Clark, J. Allen, 58, 127
Clay, Henry, 8

149